CONTENTS

THE AUTHENTIC MOTHER GOOSE
FAIRY TALES
AND
NURSERY RHYMES

JACQUES BARCHILON
AND
HENRY PETTIT

THE AUTHENTIC

MOTHER GOOSE

FAIRY TALES

AND

NURSERY RHYMES

ALAN SWALLOW
DENVER

INTRODUCTION

FAIRY TALES AND RHYMES

Nursery rhymes and fairy tales are the common treasure of children the world over. Before the advent of printing certain stories and rhymes were already widespread in Europe. Oral tradition—which implies far better memories than we have at our disposal now— ensured survival of much that was told or sung to children. Printing, in turn, was to give fixed form to this wealth of children's lore, much of which finally came down to us in the form of a few familiar classics. However, as one would readily expect, the printed text soon spread the stories and tales of childhood outside of their original geographical confines, with the result that they were translated, adapted, and incorporated in national traditions far from their birthplaces. Moreover, it became possible for countries with a flourishing oral tradition (such as Germany, Canada, and the French colony in Louisiana) to reproduce as folklore what was once a printed text. Thus the very French "Petit Chaperon Rouge" (first printed in 1697) became the very German "Rotkäppchen" which the brothers Grimm collected from the peasants' mouths and printed anew in their collection in 1812; and the familiar English rhyme:

> Jack and Jill
> Went up the hill
> To fetch a pail of water;
> Jack fell down
> And broke his crown,
> And Jill came tumbling after,

first printed in 1781, became the Danish rhyme:

> Jeck og Jill
> Vent op de hill
> Og Jell kom tombling efter.

7

The Danish text was collected as recently as 1949. If the scholar inquires, he is told "that this is one of the last discernible relics of the British occupation [of part of Denmark] during the Napoleonic war."[1] It is no wonder, then, if, because of this interplay of printed and oral texts, quite a few rhymes and tales display an extraordinary vitality. They seem to have been with us always and they will endure long after us. We accept them automatically, often without acknowledging, or even without recognizing, that many were actually the work of distinguished authors.

The present volume offers the first original texts of two English classics, the *Mother Goose Tales*[2] of Charles Perrault (the first French text was printed in 1697 and the first English translation in 1729), and the *Mother Goose's Melody* (the first edition of 1781 has disappeared but survives in the form of a 1791 reprint).

These two famous books deserve to be printed and bound in a single cover for many reasons. In the first place, both are attributed to Mother Goose. Also they contain some of the best fairy tales and nursery rhymes. Finally, the almost general ignorance of the early circumstances of the two demands that a common introduction and printing bring recognition to their literary significance. No works that have endured anonymously are more worthy of critical appraisal than these. There is surely no need to substantiate the universality of such fairy tales as "Sleeping Beauty," "Red Riding Hood," "Blue Beard," "Cinderella," "Beauty and the Beast," or of such rhymes as "Ride a cock horse," "Hickory, dickory, dock," and "Jack Sprat."

MOTHER GOOSE

Mother Goose never existed. This blunt statement has to be made right now in order to correct a persistent American legend about the Bostonian origins of our rhymes. Many misinformed New Englanders still hold fast to the notion that a woman from Boston composed a book of nursery rhymes in the early eighteenth century. While it is true that there did exist in Boston a lady called Elizabeth Goose (Vergoose or Vertigoose) she is not the inventor of the *Mother Goose's Melody*: and the claim that she gave her printer son-in-law, Thomas Fleet, a collection of rhymes which he printed in 1719 in Boston under the familiar title is spurious.[3] No copy of this volume was ever mentioned in booksellers' catalogues, nor is there any record of its having been sold anywhere, nor, indeed, was any copy of this "ghost" ever located. Despite this effort to appropriate her by New England, Mother Goose remains as elusive as the lady sitting astride the neck of a flying goose sometimes represented on the title page of children's books.

The real Mother Goose was born in France. For Mother Goose is simply the English for the French, "ma mère l'Oye." Dictionaries of the seventeenth century mention her in connection with such expressions as "contes de ma mère l'Oye," or "contes de la mère l'Oye." These dictionaries list, as equivalents of the then popular expression, "contes bleus" and "contes de vieilles." Translated, the latter expression becomes "old wives' tales," a phrase whose English flavor corresponds closely to its French connotation. Of course, the expression was a synonym for fairy tales. Thus things that were fabulous or fictitious were thought of as "contes de ma mère l'Oye" by the French, with a clear overtone of witty disparagement;[4] dictionaries also explain that our expression was but another form of the phrase "contes à dormir debout" (which is understandable, though untranslatable).

The first writer to connect Mother Goose with a collection of fairy tales was Charles Perrault. However, when his famous book appeared in 1697 the words "contes de ma mère l'Oye" were not on the title page but on the frontispiece. His more refined and "literary" title was not without its pristine charm: *Histoires ou contes du temps passé.* Because of its popular appeal *Contes de ma mère l'Oye* is the better known title, which most regularly connotes fairy tales in the minds of French children (although the expression "contes de Perrault" means just the same to them), and is also the one under which the stories have often been reprinted.

Before accounting for the passage of Mother Goose to England we should define more precisely her French origins. She is solidly rooted in folklore. Most probably the task of keeping the geese was entrusted to older women in the French village, since it was not a very strenuous chore. As a stock teller of tales any one of these goose-keeping ladies could be called "ma mère l'Oye." This is the simplest and most plausible explanation for the origin of the expression.[6]

Mother Goose came to England in 1729 when Robert Samber translated the French text of Perrault. His edition, which appeared in London, reproduced faithfully the engravings of a Dutch reprint (in French) of the same year. The Dutch reprint itself, with some changes and additions, was a reproduction of the 1697 original text. Just as the Dutch and French editions had a frontispiece showing Mother Goose as a peasant woman by a fireplace entertaining a group of three children in rapt attention, the English edition had an engraving showing the same scene, except that the words on a placard read, for the first time in English, *Mother Goose's Tales.* The formal title follows its French antecedent: *Histories or Tales of past Times.* Before the end of the century this translation had been reprinted many times in London, and it had also been issued in New England (the first American edition is that of Peter Edes of Haverhill, published in 1794) with considerable success. It is not strange, then, that Mother Goose had become a household word by 1750, when John Newbery, who became the celebrated printer of children's books, started his business. He was a resourceful man, eager to please children; he studied the "market" to find out what books would sell. What was more natural than to borrow the expression which then applied to fairy tales and use it in connection with his edition of nursery rhymes? For it was his happy idea to prepare a collection with the now famous title of *Mother Goose's Melody*, which he did not live to see in print. He died in 1767 and it was not until 1781 that publication by his successors was announced in an advertisement in the *London Chronicle* of January 2, 1781 (vol. 49, p. 5). This advertisement was repeated in the same periodical on January 18.[7] The date for the first edition has been hitherto thought to have been as early as 1765. However, no copy of such an edition has ever been found. One copy of a 1791 edition is extant and is the earliest copy of *Mother Goose's Melody* known. It is this which we now reproduce.

Such is the history of Mother Goose, from France to London and to New England, where she became so popular that some Bostonians thought that they had to invent, or reinvent, her. Before we turn to a critical discussion of the Mother Goose tales and rhymes, we must account for the meaning of the word "melody" in connection with our rhymes. Why is the word in the singular and not in the plural? Surely there must be more than *one* nursery melody. A search in seventeenth- and eighteenth-century dictionaries reveals that, strangely enough, the word seemed to be unknown in its plural form. To our modern minds it would be more logical to say "Mother Goose's Melodies" than "Mother Goose's Melody." But in the age of Doctor Johnson the word melody, in its singular form, meant "music," "harmony," or "song." It is only since the early nineteenth century that the word has acquired its more familiar meaning of rhythmic tonal qualities. Thus, while we sense rhythms and tunes in the familiar rhymes for the nursery, the contemporaries of John Newbery seemed to have been sensitive only to the general notion of song and singing in them.

THE ORIGINS OF FAIRY TALES

Fairy tales originate in folklore. They are the familiar tales most of us remember from childhood—however indistinctly—with magic elements without implicating either gods (the realm of mythology), or ghosts (the realm of the fantastic in connection with superstitions and the cult of the dead.) Since this does not usually satisfy the curiosity of those asking where fairy tales come from, because it fails to account for the universality of their themes and motifs, we can do no better than accept the hypothesis that fairy tales represent "an exteriorization of deep psychological forces. For the child, as for the adult, the apparently motiveless actions of fairies, witches and ogres can be taken to symbolize very exactly the operations of the unconscious."[8]

The psychological implications of this explanation will be more fully discussed in the next section (The Mother Goose Tales as Literature). In the meantime let us review briefly a series of texts which may or may not have influenced Charles Perrault in the conception of his tales. For these earlier versions are really analogues and cannot be considered as textual sources (there are very few resemblances in the wording of Perrault and that of his predecessors).

The first tale of the 1697 collection,[9] "La Belle au Bois Dormant" ("The Sleeping Beauty in the Wood") has a long history as motif, the enchanted spell, or sleep. Greek mythology records the long sleep of the shepherd Epimenides. The Bible, too, has its spell cast by God upon Adam. Just like the Sleeping Beauty, the first man is put to sleep and is born anew, to find his mate.[10] We follow the Sleeping Beauty motif down through the corridors of time, through the *Volsunga Saga* in which Brynhild, surrounded in her prison of fire, is delivered from enchantment by Sigurd; through the episode mentioned in the anonymous French romance of chivalry,

Perceforest[11] (published in 1538) ; and finally, through the Neapolitan author Giambattista Basile, who, in 1634-36, published his *Cunto deli cunti, overo il Pentamerone*,[12] containing a version of "Sleeping Beauty," "Sole, Lune e Talia," (that is, "Sun, Moon and Talia") very close to that of Perrault. The Neapolitan and the French are the only two authors who follow the fate of the princess after her awakening. With Latin realism they describe the involvement of the young woman with a very wicked rival (in Basile, another wife; in Perrault, an ogrish mother-in-law). The Grimm version, it will be recalled, does not elaborate on this true to life aspect of the Sleeping Beauty, since her adventures end shortly after she is discovered.

The second Perrault story, "Le Petit Chaperon Rouge" ("The Little Red Riding Hood") is remarkable in that it is not recorded before Perrault. Thus the story which critics acclaim as the most popular in flavor is without close antecedents. Faint indication of its possible existence in previous popular tradition survives in the word "chaperon" which dictionaries of the time define as a very old type of hat worn in the Middle Ages. In the opinion of these writers, at least, the possibility that Perrault invented this immortal nursery tale should not be discarded.

The tale of "La Barbe bleue" ("Blue Beard") may also be, at least in part, original; for there are no close parallels to it before Perrault. Of this story, only the theme of the tabu and the horrible fate of those breaking it was familiar in folklore and literature previous to 1697. In the *Arabian Nights* (which Perrault could not have read in his lifetime since the French translation was published one year after his death in 1704) there are many examples of the specific tabu of our story, the forbidden chamber. While there is in popular French tradition a story of a husband attempting to behead his wife (the Breton legend of Trophine) which may have inspired Perrault, the Oriental character of this story should not be overlooked. There is something of an

13

Arab husband (if seen only through Western eyes) in the cruelty of Blue Beard. Indeed, the illustrations of that story often give a peculiar headdress, turban-like, to the violent tempered man. Besides, beards were not worn in France during the later years of the seventeenth century; French minds undoubtedly associated beards with Turkish fashions. Some later versions of the tale will further emphasize the Oriental touch by calling Blue Beard's unfortunate wife "Fatima."

Insofar as "Le Chat Botté" ("Puss in Boots") is concerned its main motif is that of the animal as helper; it carries atavistic memories of the familiar totem animal as the father protector of the tribe found everywhere by missionaries and anthropologists. An Italian author of a highly succesful collection, the *Piacevolle Notti* (published in 1550-53 and many time translated in French), Gianfrancesco Straparola,[13] might have influenced Perrault. His story of "Constantino Fortunato" foreshadows strikingly the story of the resourceful cat; but the boots seem to be the invention of the French author, as there is no record of a booted cat before his version appeared.

The tale of "Les Fées" ("The Fairy") is the least known of the Perrault collection. But in folklore it has contributed the common motif known as *Kind and Unkind*. Basile wrote a prototype of it, "Le Doie Pizzelle" ("The Two Cakes"). Basically the two accounts are the same: the kind younger sister is rewarded for her behavior toward the fairy she meets at the fountain, while the unkind older sister is punished for her rudeness. In English folklore this tale is often referred to as the story of "Diamonds and Toads."

The next story is "Cendrillon" ("Cinderella"), with "Sleeping Beauty" one of the best known in Perrault's collection. This tale is fairly closely foreshadowed by Basile's "La Gatta Cenerentola" ("The Cat Cinderella"). The similarity of the sounds "Cenerentola," "Cendrillon," and "Cinderella" clearly shows that the Neapolitan author is the father of Cinderella. For Cendrillon is but a Gallic form of "Cenerentola," just as

14

"Cinderella" is an Anglicized form of "Cendrillon." "Cenerentola" derives from two Latin words for "ashes," *cinis,* and for "carry," *tollere.* Cinderella, sitting close to the hearth, is thus the ash-carrier. Both the French and the English texts will exploit this idea, the one by calling her CuCendron (Ash Bottom) and the other by saying that she is a Cinderbreech. As a tale of a persecuted step-daughter, Cinderella also has a high antiquity in folklore.

Insofar as the seventh story is concerned, "Riquet à la Houppe" ("Riquet with the Tuft") we should state at once that under this unfamiliar title we have one of the best known of tales, "Beauty and the Beast," whose roots go back to Latin literature in the first version of "Cupid and Psyche" (in Apuleius' *Golden Ass*). For this tale Perrault must have consulted an interesting version of the same title published only two years before his edition, Mlle Bernard's story published in 1695 in her novel, *Inès de Cordoue.* He may also have seen the tale of Basile's *Pentamerone* referred to as "Lo Cattenaccio" ("The Padlock").

The eighth, and last, story of the Perrault collection, "Le Petit Poucet" ("Hop o' my Thumb") is sometimes confused with the story of "Tom Thumb." The former story is close to Perrault's motif of the diminutive little boy, but it is very different in plot and incidents. Notably, in "Tom Thumb" there are no Seven Leagues Boots. However, it should be noticed that this tale is the only one which can be traced earlier in English tradition. In 1621 there appeared an English version, *The History of Thom Thumbe, the Little, for his Small Stature Surnamed, King Arthur's Dwarfe,* whose quaint title we could not resist from quoting in full.[14]

It would appear, from the number of texts we have mentioned, that the Mother Goose's tales were not entirely unkown by the time Perrault printed them. And yet it would not be wrong to say that it was thanks to him that they became known all over Europe. His collection became *the* collection. Nearly all of his stories

15

became the best examples of the given types of Sleeping Beauty, Red Riding Hood, Puss in Boots, and so on. His little book had a mighty influence.[15]

THE MOTHER GOOSE TALES
AS LITERATURE

An important part, often neglected, of a work of art is the title. To our knowledge, no critic as yet has wondered whether the titles of Perrault's tales were original. The expression "Sleeping Beauty" has gone around the world, but who remembers Perrault? While the story and the name live on, the author is forgotten. The stroke of genius was to add the gerund "dormant" and thus create a title that is at once poetic and popular. Likewise, the title "Le Petit Chaperon Rouge" with its soft alliterations is another lucky find. The very words suggest the nimble gait of a girl. Among the other six tales, three titles seem original and became widespread: "La Barbe Bleue," "Le Chat Botté," and the "Petit Poucet" (the term "le petit poucelot" is earlier found in Noel Dufail's *Propos Rustiques*). Only "Les Fées" (translated as "The Fairy") and "Riquet à la Houppe (incorporated as such in the Samber translation) are not well known. We have already commented on the ubiquitous expression, "Cinderella."

While there is a faint possibility that the discovery of earlier texts might rob Perrault of the invention of such beautiful titles, we have no reason as yet to doubt that he was their originator. Folklorists have always claimed that he did nothing more than to put into print a few very popular stories. Therefore his originality consists in having faithfully recorded the words of peasants and nurses of his age. There is no doubt concerning the opinion of his contemporaries who held that his tales must be thought of as having "for authors an infinite number of fathers, mothers, grandmothers, governesses and friends."[16] If the tales came from popular tradition, what did Perrault invent? What features of his tales are traditional and what are his? We could consult versions of his tales which circulated in oral tradition previous to the time he wrote. Usually one finds such texts among what the English call chap-books and the French *livres de colportage*. Surely enough, among these are found many fairy tales, including many volumes containing Perrault's tales; but all are subsequent to Perrault's publication and are mere reprints of his *Contes*. It seems likely that he influenced popular tradition far more than he was influenced by it.[17]

In the previous section we have discussed the basic elements, or motifs, of Perrault's tales, most of which existed before him and could be found in literary texts. The case of Perrault is unique among story tellers because one cannot tell for certain where he uses popular language and where he uses his own voice. In dealing with material from popular tradition an author has to bend his talents in two opposite directions: he must attempt to record faithfully, he must create convincingly and forcefully. In the measure that he is a recorder, he is a lesser creator. In the measure that he is creative, he loses his closeness to the folk and becomes too refined and thus less "authentic." An author who was much more a creator than a recorder, Hans Christian Andersen, won just fame for his stories of wonder, tinged with the personal accent of his wistful humor and melancholy. His understanding of children, too, is close to what modern psychology has brought to the fore since Freud called attention to the neglected and subtle influences in childhood.

Humor implies sympathy with the person being derided. In that sense it is more dignified and elevated than wit and sarcasm. It would follow, then, that the register of humor is rather limited. What is the place of satire and the comic in relation to wit and humor? In the case of Perrault one could say that humor can border on satire while handling a "soi-disant" childish wonder tale. To be able to inject so much meaning while retaining the character of a fairy tale is no mean literary achievement. The child enjoys the wonderful and the adult relishes the humor. Within the limited confines of his narrative he achieves effects that range from humorous allusions to "debunking" ironic asides, by way of Gallic innuendoes and gentle parodies of everyday manners.

In "Sleeping Beauty" when the ogrish mother-in-law orders the cooks to kill the princess whom she wants served up for dinner, the unfortunate man is rather embarrassed as to how he will fool the Queen mother by serving her a substitute animal: "[he] despaired of being able to deceive her. The young Queen was past twenty, not reckoning the hundred years that she had slept: her skin was somewhat hard, though fair and white; and how to find in the yard a beast so firm was what puzzled him. . . ."[18] There could be no wittier way of disclosing how old the princess really was than by humorously suggesting that the addition of a hundred and twenty years would certainly combine to make anyone's meat rather "hard." This is gentle burlesquing of the fantastic, which reminds us that Perrault belongs to the Baroque Period.

In "Blue Beard" we are amused to read that when the young man was dazzled by the courtship of her suitor she resolved to marry him and she "began to think, that the master of the house had not a Beard so very Blue, and that he was a very civil gentleman." It is as if this beard, a frightening symbol of virility, had suddenly become attractive, while still remaining somewhat blue, and therefore, a little threatening. This linking of a young lady's propensity to marriage with the color of a suitor's beard is a delightful insight into the workings of the female mind. Moreover, throughout the tale the relationship between the husband and his wife will be coming to the fore in such a way as to jeopardize the life of the young woman. There is no need to summarize the well known story. Improbable though it may be it conforms in some mysterious way with the logic of childhood. For a child lost in his day-dream world it does not seem strange that a husband could hack off his wife's head if she betrays him. Asked if Blue Beard had a right to kill his wife, many children answer: "but yes, because she had found his secret and disobeyed him." Because Perrault knew children well and feared they might take his story too seriously, he offered the relief of humor by pointing to the fictitiousness of his tale. The moral of "Blue Beard" reads:

> A very littel share of common sense
> And knowledge of the world, will soon evince,
> That this is a story of time long past,
> No husbands now such panick terrors cast;
> Nor weakly, with a vain despotick hand,
> Imperious, what's impossible, command:
> And be they discontented, or the fire
> Of wicked jealousy their hearts inspire,
> They softly sing; and of whatever hue
> Their beard may chance to be, or black or blue,
> Grizzled or russet, it is hard to say
> Which of the two, the man or the wife, bears sway.

While the translation is accurate the extra ounce of wit from the French, "On voit bien-tost que cette histoire est un conte du temps passé," did not pass into English; for the expression "a story of time long past" does not have the full flavor of the Perrault original.

In "The Fairy" the king's son, at the end of the story, meets the kind younger sister who had been turned out of doors by her stepmother because she spewed diamonds (while her sister could only spew toads). He is rather astonished to see her cry while diamonds and pearls fall out of her mouth. He asks the pretty maid to explain things to him: "She accordingly told him the whole story; upon which the King's son fell in love with her; and considering with himself that such a gift as this was worth more than any marriage portion whatsoever in another, conducted her to the palace of the King his father, and there married her." Here is a practical young man who knows a girl of property when he sees one; yet a girl spewing diamonds is something supernatural which somehow does not tally with the down-to-earth attitude of the prince. Humor, in this instance, brings us to the borderland of the fantastic and the real.

Within this dream world extraordinary things happen, but Perrault will again and again deny the wonderful by means of witty digressions. Probably the most famous of these is the one in the tale of "Riquet à la Houppe" where we are informed that no fairy effected the transformation of the ugly Riquet into a handsome man. It was all the work of love.

> Some authors affirm, that this was not owing to the charms of the Fairy, which worked this change, but love alone caused the Metamorphosis. They say, that the Princess having made the reflection . . . on her lover . . . saw no longer the deformity of his body, nor the ugliness of his face; that his hump seem'd to her no more than the air of one who had a broad back; and that whereas till then she saw him frightfully lame, she found it nothing more than a certain bending air, which charm'd her. They say further, that his eyes which were very squinting, seem'd to her most bright and sparkling. . . .

This kind of humor has a liberating and enobling effect; it gently reminds man of his foibles. Here Perrault seems closer to such authors as the earlier Spanish Cervantes, or the later English author Fielding, than his French contemporaries.

But in the realm of veiled erotic suggestions, he is very French, as could be expected: The two tales of "Sleeping Beauty" and "Red Riding Hood" are interesting in this respect. The very idea of a beautiful young woman helpless in lethargy suggests erotic possibilities, which the Italian and French forerunners of Perrault were not remiss to exploit. Both Basile and the anonymous author of the French *Perceforest* tell how the sleeping princess was ravished during her sleep, only to awaken after delivery of the children she was unaware of having conceived. This erotic aspect of the story is driven underground by Perrault and only humor suggests what may have been in Perrault's mind and that of his contemporaries. After the princess awakens, without waiting for life's normal delay, within a few hours she is married. The story teller was probably smiling inside when he wrote that they slept "very little; the Princess had no occasion." As in the other two authors mentioned above, the Perrault version makes quite clear that the prince had a secret love for a considerable time before openly declaring his marriage to his mother and his people. This conformity with earlier models suggests that Perrault knew the other versions and it shows that the nature of his genius was such that he refined upon the earlier coarse and somewhat Rabelaisian material. In the moral of the tale he will again stress the erotic with his characteristic humor.

> To get a husband rich, genteel and gay,
> Of humor sweet, some time to stay,
> Is natural enough, 'tis true.
> But then to wait a hundred years,
> And all that while asleep, appears
> A thing intirely new.
> Now at this time of day,
> Not one of the sex we see
> To sleep with such profound tranquility.

In "Red Riding Hood" the whole cannibalistic story appears to be a tale told on two levels: the literal, for children's consumption, and the symbolic, for the merriment of the adult story teller or listener. This treatment not only provides a gay note but even dramatic irony. For we cannot fail to be moved when we read that the "wolf had a good mind to eat her up." We know what the child-woman does not know, that she will be eaten up, that is, seduced, within the moment. While the child understands readily that the little girl is in peril because "she did not know how dangerous a thing it is to stay and hear a Wolfe talk," the adult chuckles because his wolf is a horse of another color. The celebrated dialogue with the wolf-man is but an anticipation of

21

seduction when the child-woman is surprised at the shape of her would-be grandmother, "she was very much astonished to see how her grandmother looked in her night-cloaths" (the more "risqué" French text has the word "deshabillé"). Finally, to make this cannibalistic story equate a seduction, the moral will point out that "growing ladies fair . . . ill do they listen to all sorts of tongues . . . no wonder therefore . . . if overpowr'd so many of them has the Wolfe devour'd."

Three centuries later James Thurber was to write his own witty version of this tale in which he clearly explained how young ladies can protect themselves from ensnaring wolves (in his *Fables For Our Times*). We hardly ever think of it, but it is most probable that the notion of a young man as seducer of young ladies came to be labeled a wolf only after the appearance of Perrault's story in English.

Perrault's use of irony and humor is so subtle that his narrative is never retarded by it. The main thing is the story and he gets on with it at a fast pace. In order not to slow down the tale his irony is often confined to little parodies of manner while telling something which belongs to the supernatural. For instance, the father of Sleeping Beauty is not the least astonished to see the fairy godmother of his daughter arrive "in a fiery chariot, pulled by dragons." The spectacle might surprise anyone but this urbane king who finds it quite natural; so, "he handed her out of the chariot." This contrast between the fantastic and the very polite behavior of the king produces a delicate parody of both the fairy tale and the everyday world.

Similar effects turn up in the strange concern of the fairy for what would happen (in a hundred years) to the princess when she would awaken, "as she had a very great foresight, she thought when the Princess should awake she might not know what to do with herself, being all alone in this old palace." Indeed, it was a great foresight; for, as we know, the whole palace, from the scullions to the little dog of the princess, were put to

22

sleep, "that they might be ready to wait upon her when she wanted them." One can imagine the children of Perrault (he was a devoted father, having become a widower after only six years of marriage) asking for details about the other members of the palace; obligingly, the old man would explain what did happen to the others. This kind hearted concern results in the sort of realism which delights the young ones and amuses the grown up (children).

Sometimes the humor of Perrault verges on satire. The king's daughter in "Puss in Boots" did not take long to fall in love with the Marquis de Carabas (in reality the miller's son all dressed up in borrowed clothes through the ingenuity of his cat) : "as the fine clothes . . . had set off his good mien (for he was well made, and very handsome in his person) the King's daughter took a secret inclination to him, and the Marquis of *Carabas* had no sooner cast two or three respectful and somewhat tender glances, but she fell in love with him to distraction." What stands out in humorous contrast is the opportunism of the young man and the "romantic" feelings of the princess. The moral of the tale will show that it was this opportunism which appealed to Perrault, good Frenchman that he was.

> If a miller's son gains so sudden the heart
> Of a beautiful Princess, and makes her impart
> Sweet languishing glances, eyes dying for love,
> It must be remarked of fine clothes how they move.
> And that youth, a good face, a good air and mien
> Are not always indifferent mediums to win
> The heart of the fair, and gently inspire
> The flames of tender passion, and tender desire.

Interesting as these instances of humor are, they still pale when compared to the most characteristic of Perrault which are found in the charming episode of the transformations in "Cinderella." It will be recalled that when the fairy godmother appears she provides Cinderella with a coach, footmen, clothes, and all the equipment necessary to go to the ball in regal circumstances.

Critics of Perrault have been quick to point out that the transformation of a pumpkin into a coach, lizards into footmen, has a strong logical basis. The fairies of Perrault have been called Cartesian; for after all, it is only logical to take a round object like a pumpkin and make a coach of it, since its round shape already anticipates that of the coach. Similarly, the solemn lizards already suggest the liveried footmen with their coat tails trailing behind their backs. By such a nice concern for logical analogies an author is sure to captivate the imagination of the child, who wants his fancy firmly rooted in reality. Also true to children's psychology is the love of details and enumerations which Perrault satisfies so well in "Cinderella." In no other tale does Perrault show more originality than in the touching adventures of the persecuted step-child. A most fascinating aspect of the story is the duality of the personality of Cinderella who is both a very little girl and a woman. She is very child-like when "her godmother, who saw her in tears, asked her what was the matter? I wish I could . . . I wish I could . . . she could not speak the rest, her tears interrupting her. Her godmother, who was a Fairy, said to her, Thou wishest thou could'st go to the ball, it is not so? Y . . . es, said Cinderilla, with a great Sob. Well, said her godmother, be but a good girl, and I'll contrive thou shalt go." This text is alive and *real*.

The Cinderella of Perrault has a vivid personality. One wonders if she was not patterned after one of the daughters of Perrault himself. Here she is, having caught the excitement of the magical game: "As she was at a loss for a coach-man. I'll go and see, says Cinderilla, if there be never a rat in the rat trap, we'll make a coach-man out of him. You are in the right, said her godmother, go and see." True enough, there was a rat "which had the largest beard" and which became (logically) "a fat jolly coach-man, that had the finest whiskers as ever were seen." The child that was playing with her godmother has now became a regal lady; she is led by the King's son "into the hall where the company was: there was a great silence; they left off dancing, and the violins ceased to play, so attentive was every body to contemplate the beauties of this unknown person: there was heard nothing but a confused noise of ha! how handsome she is, ha! how handsome she is! The king himself, as old as he was could not help looking at her . . ."

The genius of Perrault consists in narrating wonderful events while always keeping a sure hand on the real feelings of his characters. His characters move in the supernatural with the assurance of living persons. He artfully juxtaposes the wonderful and the real. The finished product is a tale in which the extraordinary has the plausibility of the true to life. As in dreams, an effective suspension of disbelief is effected. Even humor participates in the wonderful world, even if it sometimes contradicts the supernatural. Humor simply introduces an element of playful doubt which is the essence of dramatic enjoyment. By the end of the tale the child has grown and reached maturity and with it the freedom and happiness which he seeks in his imprisoned childish state. Perrault was fully aware of the function of the fairy tale; he conceived of the supernatural story as a healthy diversion which does good to the child, appealing, lulling, diverting, and satisfying the cravings of his imagination. Even the sadistic element is part of the lesson to be given, the tale helping the child anticipate the deeper mysteries of life which he will fully encompass in later years. Perrault is an author with integrity toward both the soul of man and that of the child. In his own words:

> It is not praiseworthy of fathers and mothers, when the children are not yet old enough to taste strong unpleasant truths, to make them like them, and if I may put it this way, to make them swallow them by enveloping them in tales that are pleasant and suited to their tender years? It is unbelievable how these innocent souls, whose natural goodness has not yet been corrupted, receive these subtle teachings. We see them sad and depressed as long as the hero or the heroine is un-

lucky, and shouting with joy when the time for their happiness arrives; in the same way, having endured impatiently the prosperity of the wicked man or woman, they are overjoyed when they see them finally punished as they deserve.[19]

Perrault well understood that the rich imagination of the child enables him to let himself be projected into any situation. He identifies himself with the characters of the fairy tale and they and their environment become wish fulfillments. He becomes the happy prince in "Sleeping Beauty," or the soon to be happy Cinderella; he follows with interest the adventures of Puss in Boots and his master; he also experiences fear and suspense in such a story as "Blue Beard." For the child, the distinction between fiction and reality is at first almost non-existent. A child accepts the fairy tale as something that may have happened "long ago, when fairies existed." Perrault probably had the same idea in mind when he wrote that fairy tales, although contrary to reason and common sense, charm and educate the mind better than moralistic sermons or realistic stories.[20]

It is doubtful whether Perrault would fully endorse what modern psychoanalysts see in the fairy tale; but, we believe that, dimly, he was aware of their deeper unconscious meaning and message. Psychoanalysts hold that the child, through the comparison between the fantastic and the real, gradually learns to test reality. When the child realizes that the fairy tale is fictitious he learns to enjoy it as fiction. This is one giant step not only in the process of rational maturation but in esthetic development as well. For he becomes aware of the distinction between the stage and reality.

Eventually he craves more and more fiction, more and more of the fairy tales which the adult offers him because he adopts the fairy tale and incorporates it in the fabric of his dreams. In fact, he soon prefers the fairy tale to his own fancies: it is artistically more beautiful and therefore more satisfying.

This process seems natural enough; but when the

adult examines the fairy tale carefully, he will be somewhat astonished to find how wicked the mother-in-law can be in "Sleeping Beauty," how sadistic and cruel Blue Beard can be, how transparent and crude the symbolism of "Red Riding Hood," how sordid and selfish Tom Thumb can be (when he causes the ogre's daughter to be killed, and eventually robs the ogre of all his fortune). Understandably the adult is disappointed in his vision of the child as "pure." He might go so far as to remove fairy tales from the reach of his children. By so doing he would act stupidly; for he will have forgotten that the child knows full well the difference between fiction and reality. In fact, the fairy tale is the more enjoyable because the child knows it is fictitious. The adult (even if he does not have a psychiatrist at hand) should understand that the veiled symbolism of the fairy tale and its violence fulfill a need in the child's life. The fairy tale is his apprenticeship to life. This is why the bad stepmother, the merciless king, or the cruel ogre are all part of his world; they are the creations of his own mind. No wonder if

His fears and feeling of guilt, his hopes and desires find their expression in this world. From clinical experience we know that in those dreams of adults which are the unveiling of the fantasies of early childhood, fairy tales tend to express what for the child's own life once had a vital importance (Freud, 1913). The fairy tale theme was in most of these cases chosen by the child as less dangerous and less forbidden; it was not a product of his own imagination, but a pattern for his emotional reactions offered to him with the consent of the adults.[21]

Removed from us in time, the fairy tales of Perrault recreate immemorial dreams in the setting of castles, palaces, peasants' homes, forests, and fields of the seventeenth century. These reflections of long gone days do not shine weakly through the now tarnished mirrors of the *Galerie des Glaces* of Versailles. They shine with a radiance of their own through the mirage of words poetically endowed. These *Histories of Past Times* have the added charm of that world from beyond, the dream. What Perrault did was to create a world in which our sense of reality and discrimination becomes temporarily blurred through the dramatic and esthetic illusion. If his princesses, his peasants, and his talking animals seem to wander through a tale as we would through a dream it is because he has graced them with just the necessary ounce of waking consciousness which renders the fantasy credible. The appeal of Perrault's tales to young and old, from widely distant lands, comes from the fact that they permit expression of nearly universal wishes present in both the dreaming and the waking state. These become plausible because he made them compatible with the the social and moral standards of our culture. Perhaps Perrault's fairy tales correspond to his own dreams and wishes (perhaps he was simply the vehicle of an inspiration of genius) moulded into a felicitous literary form which is at once expressive of his talent and the inner mind of civilized man. His sophistication becomes striking, as we have seen, when his stories are compared to earlier and cruder forms. Basile's tale of "Sun, Moon and Talia," for instance, is but an outlet for a young man's unbridled desires, while Perrault's "Sleeping Beauty" is made acceptable to a late seventeenth-century French audience when she is married to her discoverer. Thus the behavior of the pair is all that respectability would demand. Yet (as we do know), the wording of the story leaves enough to suggest precisely what Perrault may have eliminated from the less disguised earlier versions. There is a marriage, but it is on the very first day, and "sans perdre de temps" (these words are in the text), with disregard for real life delays. Such hastiness—and other humorous innuendoes we called attention to—attests that the erotic feeling was not lost in Perrault, but merely restated without being completely repressed.

Had Perrault avoided completely such elements, the hidden vicarious gratification of the fairy tale would have been denied his audience. How else could we explain that children enjoy such a sadistic story as "Blue

Beard," or that adults smile when they read "Red Riding Hood," if we do not assume that there is already present in child and grownup alike an undercurrent of violence and unchecked sexual appetite which the fairy tale satisfies symbolically. Perrault's genius enables him to modify violence and sex sufficiently to make them acceptable yet attractive.

We have seen what devices he uses to attenuate the basic brutality of his situations; by being humorous or witty he allows the reader to become his esthetic accomplice in pleasure. Such is the mark of the sensitive writer aware that he suggests some of the most threatening situations in life by keeping a light touch (the same touch which will be found in Andersen). Furthermore, the very fact that these tales were supposedly written by a child (Perrault's son Pierre Darmancour) and for other children allows the adult to enjoy them without guilt: one could say, "These are childish bagatelles, not literature."

The final touch of the writer highly conscious of his art was to append seemingly ethical justifications to his stories in his morals, as a last device to excuse adult enjoyment of such "puerile" matter. This must have been felt necessary in a century so anxious to appear rational as that of Perrault, but seemed incongruous in the Romantic times of Sainte-Beuve; so much so that the nineteenth century critic refused to believe, in his review of the tales, that they could have come from the same mind as that which wrote the stories.

Finally, we hardly need to state how fully we endorse the psychoanalytic view of the fairy tale as a dream to be unveiled. We can agree that the fantasy of both dreams and fairy tales has a common function. Just as the dream expresses innermost wishes in a disguised form, the fairy tale masks our real wishes with the appearance of a free fantasy. The great merit of Perrault's artistry consists precisely in having made such a disguise—of the very stuff of literary craft, style—invisible at first view.

THE MOTHER GOOSE RHYMES
AS LITERATURE

Nursery rhymes first heard in childhood return to our memories from some deep pit of forgetfulness. With their haunting sing-song rhythms they surge forth at unexpected moments. The world of rhymes is the same as that of fairy tales, wonderful, irrational, violent, and dream-like. In the words of that inspired critic, V. Sackville-West, the nursery "is the place where, if blackbirds can sing in pies, as they undoubtedly can, there is no inherent reason why a whole rookery should not fly out of a beard. . . . It puts to shame the real world, where the number of things that can happen, must, after all, be finite, with the attendant dullness resulting from the predictable."[22]

Over and beyond all this, nursery rhymes have poetical value. The first sounds English-speaking children hear and are taught to say open the golden realm of poetically meant language to beings who are scarcely able to babble. This experience is thoroughly lacking in the education of children of the Latin races. Very few of the rhymes which French children learn, for instance, are as poetic as the nursery rhymes of England and America. Such lines as "How care I how black I be?" or "When I was a little boy, I lived by myself" are truly poetic and are echoed in the purely melodic lines of such poets as Blake, Wordsworth, or Keats. In our own century, the studied simplicity of Gertrude Stein and the rhythms of A. A. Milne are unquestionably indebted to the tradition of rhymes.

The volume of *Mother Goose's Melody* we offer here is important not only for the number of rhymes it contains (fifty-two) but also for the number of times that it has been reprinted in England and the United States. In America Mother Goose has come to be indissolubly linked with nursery rhymes. Any American asked if he has heard of Mother Goose will immediately say, "of course, the children's rhymes," and will proceed to quote a few from memory. But this same American would be hard put to say who wrote the rhymes.

There is external, as well as internal, evidence pointing to the likelihood that Oliver Goldsmith was involved in their writing. Goldsmith had worked for John Newbery, doing much hackwork for him; the two were good friends and it is well known that Goldsmith liked not only nursery rhymes but childen as well. His favorite rhyme was that of "The old woman tossed in a blanket." On record there is someone who remembered being taught to play "Jack and Jill" by Goldsmith himself.[23]

The elaborate subtitle, speaking of "Lullabies of the old British Nurses, calculated to amuse Children and to excite them to Sleep," the would-be scholarly introduction, which concludes with the following "tongue in cheek" statement, "Let none therefore speak irreverently of this antient maternity [of the rhymes], as they may be considered as the great grandmothers of science and knowledge," argue in favor of Goldsmith. It is his style and his humour. Moreover, there are, for nearly each rhyme, satirical comments of a pseudo-philosophical and moralistic intent which have exactly the same function as the witty morals of Perrault's *Tales*. The commentary is again the revenge of adult wit upon the nonsensicality of childish doggerel.

Here are two examples of rhymes with their comments:

> There was an old woman
> Liv'd under a hill,
> And if she isn't gone
> She lives there still.

This is a self evident proposition, which is the very essence of truth. She lived under a hill, and if she is not gone she lives there still. Nobody will presume to contradict this.

Shoe the colt
Shoe the colt,
Shoe the wild mare;
Here a nail,
There a nail,
Yet she goes bare.

Ay, Ay, drive the nail that will go: that's the way of the world, and it is the method pursued by all our financiers, politicians and necromancers.

It is clear that the absurdity of the commentary is only apparently extraneous to the rhymes themselves. It seems to be the humorous attitude of the adult saying, "Come, Come, all this is nonsense, but let us have fun anyway." In no small measure these witty comments must have something to do with the success of the book. The *Mother Goose's Melody* contains enough to please both young and old. Such wit and humor cannot be purely conventional, it is literary work and it points again to the creative mind of such an author as Goldsmith.

The question to ask is the following. In the rhymes, how much is Goldsmith's? Undoubtedly, many rhymes here printed were already known. Of the fifty-two rhymes contained in the volume, twenty-three appear for the first time; the other twenty-nine rhymes had already been printed in earlier broadside sheets, collections of songs, and in an earlier collection of nursery rhymes, *Tommy Thumb's Pretty Song Book* (c. 1744). Is it possible to say that Goldsmith composed twenty-three new rhymes? The answer will never be known. He may have been inspired by earlier rhymes or songs. In this case, he deserves credit for the originality of a new way to present the familiar. For instance, the famous rhyme of the old woman tossed in a blanket (which appears for the first time in *Mother Goose's Melody*) may well have been meant as a "spoof" of an old song, known in the seventeenth century, *The Jacobite tossed in a blanket*. Actually, it would not have been difficult for a man with the talent for mimicry of Goldsmith to invent new rhymes with zest and wit.

Among the rhymes attributable to Goldsmith, many deserve discussion; they are interesting *per se* and in relation to their appended commentary or maxim. For instance:

> There was an old man
> And he had a calf,
> And that's half;
> He took him out of the stall,
> And put him on the wall,
> And that's all.

Maxim. Those who are given to tell all they know, generally tell more than they know.

Clearly, the rhyme is not supposed to make sense, and the maxim even less, thoroughly unrelated as it is to the sense or nonsense of the rhyme. In this maxim, and in many others, there seems to be a conscious intent at satirizing the then fashionable but heavy Johnsonian scholarship. The best way to do so was to write ponderously rational footnotes which meant nothing at all. That this intent was in the editor's mind is only too obvious from the comment which follows the rhymes "Seesaw, Margery Daw." The attack on footnotes is direct and pointed, "It is a mean and scandalous practice in authors to put notes to things that deserve no notice." But, surely enough, our author will not resist the temptation, for our delight. Quite often, however, the maxim will be morally valid and not devoid of a strong and earthy flavor. The following "Plato's Song" tells a story, with charmingly appropriate language, suited to a child, and adds a psychologically true moral.

> Ding dong bell,
> The cat is in the well.
> Who put her in?
> Little *Johnny Green.*
>
> What a naughty boy was that,
> To drown poor Pussy cat.
> Who never did any harm,
> And kill'd the mice in his father's barn.

Maxim. He that injures one threatens a hundred.

Nothing can be added, nothing further need be expanded upon, the tale is told with its little conclusion and together they form a little masterpiece.

In contrast, there are rhymes which are simply jingles in which the rhythm and rhymes, the nonsense rather than the sense, is all that matters. The following is significant in that it disturbed the Quakers who made the mistake of trying to amend it by turning it into reasonable sense, "which is the last thing that any child desires."[24] First, the rhyme and its original moral:

> High diddle diddle,
> The cat and the fiddle,
> The cow jump'd over the moon;
> The little dog laugh'd
> To see such craft,
> And the dish ran away with the spoon.

It must be a little dog that laugh'd, for a great dog would be ashamed to laugh at such nonsense.

Now for the rhyme as amended by the Quakers:

> Hey diddle diddle
> The cat and the fiddle,
> (*Yes, thee may say that, for that is nonsense,*)
> The cow jumped over the moon.
> (*Oh no, Mary, thee mustn't say that, for that is a falsehood; thee knows a cow could never jump over the moon; but a cow may jump under it, so thee ought to say*
> The cow jumped *under* the moon.)
>
> The little dog laughed . . .
> (*Oh, Mary, stop, How can a little dog laugh? Thee knows a little dog can't laugh. Thee ought to say,*
> The little dog *barked*. . . .)
>
> And the dish ran after the spoon . . .
> (*Stop, Mary, stop! A dish could never run after a Spoon. Thee had better say . . .*)

The only thing that can be said for this attempt to inject sense into the rhyme is that it ends in being supercilious, if quaint. But all the poetry and romance has been taken away. The rhymes are not to be analyzed in terms of logic, commonsense, or moral value. The grossest mistake is to believe that their nonsensicality and often sadistic content can be "corrupting." One educator concludes an article by advising parents to "put the book on some rather inaccessible shelf," because it is a work permeated with "violence, corruption, indolence, cynicism, pessimism, and anti-intellectualism." Let us not attempt to rise to the level of this educator, but leave him on his moral pedestal.[25]

The rhymes are simply flashes of tingling gaiety, cheerful and light. They can have the warmth and tenderness of mother-love:

> Hush-a-by baby
> On the tree-top,
> When the wind blows
> The cradle will rock;
> When the bough breaks
> The cradle will fall,
> Down tumbles baby,
> Cradle and all.

Since this is sung to a baby, he need not fear to fall or tumble because he does not understand the words. The mother or nurse can have her fun while singing this to a familiar tune. The maxim seems again rather unrelated. But perhaps, by a devious way, the words, "Content turns all it touches into gold," may well have a link with mother-love. All we need to do is to substitute the word *love* for the word *content,* and the maxim acquires a meaning quite connected to the rhyme.

One of the most famous rhymes, "Dickery Dickery Dock," appears also for the first time in *Mother Goose's Melody* and is a good example of ludicrous rhyme which delights the child. In America the first word *Dickery* has been changed to *Hickory*. Here is the original text.

> Dickery, dickery, dock
> The mouse ran up the clock;
> The clock struck one,
> The mouse ran down,
> Dickery, dickery dock.

Maxim. Time stays for no man.

This rhyme is the last one of the collection, and terminates Part I of the book. Part II contains sixteen lullabies selected with sure taste and discrimination from the plays of Shakespeare. The editor knew what would be appropriate for the child. Such lullabies as "When the bees suck," "Tell me where is fancy bred," or "Blow, blow, thou winter wind," have a poetic kinship with our rhymes. The greatest poet of the English language is rightly associated with the best rhymes of the nursery.

It is hoped that enough examples have been cited to bring out the poetic qualities of *Mother Goose's Melody.* Truly, those who have been raised with these rhymes enjoy a bond of intimacy; those who have not known the rhymes in childhood cannot understand each other in the same way as an Australian, a Britisher, and an American can understand each other. Those who know the rhymes belong to the great fraternity of the English-speaking peoples.

At an early age, in a way unknown to Latin peoples, Englishmen and Americans are introduced to that sonorous and poetic language. The rhymes are not prayer, but are akin to it through sheer incantatory power. As Paul Hazard rightly says, the rhymes "are not unconscious of the fact that by placing rhythm at the beginning of life they are conforming to the general order of the universe."[26] This rhythm and this music we would like to emphasize in conclusion.

The rhythm of Mother Goose is quantitative: there are beats, or accents, which are as strictly regular as the ticking of a clock, or the beating of a drum. These beats recur at regular intervals, no matter how long or how short the verse. Thus,

> There *was* an old *wom*an tossed *up* in a *blank*et
> *Seven*teen *times* as *high* as the *moon*

> *Pease*—porridge *hot,*
> *Pease* Porridge *in* the pot,
> *Nine* days *old.*

> *Sing* a song of *six*-pence

In the first example, time is marked as if by a metronome, even though the lines are of unequal lengths (twelve and nine syllables); in the second example, the regularity of the accent is metrically kept, at the expense of logical emphasis (*in,* an unimportant word, is emphasized rather than *pot,* the rhyme to *hot*). The third example offers one of the favorite devices of Mother Goose, alliteration. Another famous example, with beautiful alliterations and rhymes, is "Jack and Jill."

There is nothing children like more than this rhythmical regularity. Those who will become poets first learn the sense and rhythm of the language from Mother Goose. But rhythm is not all, there is its complement, music and melody. When we analyse the rhymes musically, we find that their general tempo is a smoothly flowing *andante,* with an almost exact correspondence of syllables to musical notes. For instance, in "Ride a Cock horse to Banbury Cross," sixteenth notes are the smallest divisions, and most are eighth notes. It is a song built on three chords, a tonic leading into a subdominant, then a tonic leading into a dominant, then a dominant seventh leading into a tonic; the final resolution is emphasized from dominant seventh to a tonic. The musical effects are simple: a dramatic setting composed of longer six-eighth rhythms approximating musically the motion of a galloping horse (as a child might play it). There is a rise in pitch to emphasize a point (*Lady, horse, wherever she goes*). The general impression is one of motion and gaiety, with crescendoes and diminuendoes to accent dramatic effects. The tempo of this particular piece is an *allegretto con spirito* which admirably fits the mood of the text.

Of course, this musical analysis is that of the rhyme as sung today. For an idea of the sound of the rhymes in the late eighteenth century we can only reproduce the musical score given in the preface to illustrate the "Old woman tossed in a blanket":

There was an old woman
    toss'd in a blanket,
Seventeen times as high as
    the moon;
But where she was going no
    mortal could tell,
For under her arm she
    carried a broom.
Old woman, old woman,
    old woman, said I?
Whither, ah whither, ah
    whither so high?
To sweep the cobwebs
    from the sky,
And I'll be with you by
    and by.

Those familiar with the tune to which the rhyme is sung today will not recognize the sounds they know. For one thing, we have difficulty in fitting the words to the music. It seems that words were made to fit the music rather than the music invented to suit the words. One wonders how an eighteenth century child could sing to such a tune. The music of the rhymes seems to have evolved during the past two centuries. It has evolved in order to become simpler, more rhythmically in tune with the simple words. At the present state of research we can say no more about the music of Mother Goose.[27] A study is now under progress and will be published in the near future. But we can safely say that the rhymes are as musical as they are poetic. They certainly satisfy the ear and they are memorable because they do. In conclusion,

> Not by history, not by mythology, not by folklore, not even by the absurdity of situations, not even by the sense of power so flatteringly suggested when by one line we can magnify a shoe into the size of a house; by their little gift of poetry and music do the nursery rhymes abide in our hearts.[28]

NOTES

[1]Iona and Peter Opie, *The Oxford Dictionary of Nursery Rhymes* (Oxford: The Clarendon Press, 1951), p. 11.

[2]Charles Perrault, *Histories or Tales of Past Times,* translated by Robert Samber (London: J. Pote and R. Montagu), 1729. [*Mother Goose's Tales* as a title appears in the frontispiece.]

[3]For fuller details see *The Oxford Dictionary of Nursery Rhymes,* pp. 37-42.

[4]It could be argued that the same connotation survives in English in the phrase, "don't be a goose."

[5]The book was published in Paris by Claude Barbin in January 1697. One story, "La Belle au bois dormant" ("Sleeping Beauty") had previously been published, with variants, in the February 1696 issue of the *Mercure Galant.*

[6]For this explanation of the origin of the phrase, we are indebted to the English linguist and scholar, John Orr (letter of May 18, 1954 to Jacques Barchilon).

[7]We are indebted to the note of M. J. P. Weedon, "Mother Goose's Melody," in *The Library,* Fifth Series, Vol. VI, Nos. 3/4, December 1951 (Oxford University Press), for the above information.

[8]Geoffrey Brereton, ed. and translator, *The Fairy Tales of Charles Perrault* (Penguin Books: 1957), p. xi.

[9]There is a recently discovered 1695 manuscript of the Perrault collection. See, Jacques Barchilon, *Perrault's Tales of Mother Goose,* The Dedication Manuscript of 1695 Reproduced in Collotype Fasimile with Introduction and Critical Text. (2 volumes published by The Pierpont Morgan Library: New York, 1956).

[10]On Adam's sleep, see Theodor Reik, *The Creation of Woman* (New York: George Braziller, 1960).

[11]For extracts and comments on this interesting work, see Jeanne Lods, *Le roman de Perceforest* (Geneva: Droz, 1951)

[12]For a translation and critical comments, see Norman Moseley Penzer, *The Pentamerone of Giambattista Basile* . . . now edited with a preface (London and New York: E. P. Dutton, 1932).

[13]The first French translation of Straparola is that of Pierre de la Rivey, *Les Nuictz Facetieuses* (Paris: Abel l'Angelier, 1585).

[14]A unique copy of this tale is owned by the Pierpont Morgan Library.

[15]For the influence of Perrault, Stith Thompson's *The Folktale* (New York: The Dryden Press, 1946) may be consulted.

[16]*Mercure Galant*, January 1697, notice on publication of the Perrault *Contes*.

[17]Concerning French chap-books and oral tradition, see Pierre Brochon, *Le Livre de colportage* (Paris: Gründ, 1954).

[18]This quotation, and all the others from Perrault's tales which follow reproduce verbatim the text of the Samber translation printed in this volume.

[19]This translation from a passage of the 1695 preface of Perrault's verse tales ("Grisélidis," "Peau d'Ane" and "Les Souhaits ridicules") is reproduced from Paul Hazard's *Books, Children and Men* (Boston: The Horn Book, 1944), p. 45.

[20]Charles Perrault, *Paralelle des anciens et des modernes* (Paris: Coignard, 1688-1696), II, 126.

[21]Ernest Kris, *Psychoanalytic Explorations in Art* (New York: International Universities Press, 1952), pp. 42-43.

[22]V. Sackville-West, *Nursery Rhymes* (London: The Dropmore Press, 1947), p. 2.

[23]See p. 34 of the *Oxford Dictionary of Nursery Rhymes*.

[24]V. Sackville-West, *op. cit.*, p. 48, quotes the text of the Quaker version.

[25]John Nadeau, "Mother Goose Exposed!" *Education*, Vol. 80, No. 8 (April 1960), 491.

[26]*Op. cit.*, p. 81.

[27]For the musical analysis of the rhymes, we are indebted to Robert Neely, a graduate student at the University of Colorado.

[28]V. Sackville-West, *op. cit.*, p. 66.

BIBLIOGRAPHY

General Works on Children's Literature

Barchilon, Jacques. "Beauty and the Beast, From Myth to Fairy Tale," *Psychoanalysis and the Psychoanalytic Review,* Volume 46, No. 4 (Winter 1959-60).

Brochon, Pierre. *Le livre de colportage en France depuis le XVIIème siècle.* Paris: Gründ, 1954.

Cahoon, Herbert. *Children's Literature, Books and Manuscripts.* An Exhibition, November 19, 1954 through February 28, 1955. New York: The Pierpont Morgan Library, 1954.

Freud, Sigmund. "The Occurrence in Dreams of Material from Fairy Tales," *Collected Papers,* translated under supervision of Joan Riviere, Volume IV. London: Hogarth Press, 1946.

————. *The Interpretation of Dreams,* in *The Basic Writings of Sigmund Freud.* New York: The Modern Library, 1938.

Hazard, Paul. *Books, Children and Men.* Translated from the French by Margaret Mitchell. Boston: The Horn Book, 1944.

Kris, Ernest. *Psychoanalytic Explorations in Art.* New York: International Universities Press, 1952.

Muir, Percival H. *English Children's Books, 1600-1900.* London: Batsford, 1954.

Reik, Theodor. *The Creation of Woman.* New York: Georges Braziller, 1960.

Róheim, Géza. "Fairy Tales and Dreams," in *The Psychoanalytic Study of the Child,* Volume 7, New York, International Press, 1953.

————. "Psychoanalysis and the Folktale," *International Journal of Psychoanalysis,* Volume III (1922).

————. *Gates of the Dream.* New York: International Universities Press, 1952.

Thompson, Stith. *The Folktale.* New York: The Dryden Press, 1946.

Perrault and His Tales

Basile, Giambattista. *The Pentamerone of Giambattista Basile,* translated with an introduction by Norman Moseley Penzer. London and New York: Dutton, 1932.

Bernard, Catherine. *Inés de Cordone.* Paris: Jouvenel, 1696.

41

De Visé, Donneau. *Mercure Galant,* Notice on publication of Perrault's *Contes* (January, 1697).

Hallays, André. *Les Perrault.* Paris: Perrin, 1926.

Henriot, Émile. *Contes de Perrault en Prose et en Vers,* publiés d'après les éditions originales avec une introduction. Paris: Chronique des Lettres Françaises, 1928.

Lods, Jeanne. *Le roman de Perceforest.* Geneva: Droz, 1951.

Perrault, Charles. *Grisélidis, Nouvelle, avec le conte de Peau d'Asne et celuy de Souhaits Ridicules.* Quatrième édition. Paris: Coignard, 1695.

————. "La Belle au bois dormant," *Mercure Galant* (February, 1696).

————. *Histoires ou contes du temps passé.* Paris: Claude Barbin. 1697.

————. *Paralelle des anciens et des modernes.* Paris: Coignard, 1688-1696. 4 vols.

————. *Histoires ou contes du temps passé,* avec des Moralitez, par Monsieur Perrault, Nouvelle Édition augmentée d'une Nouvelle à la fin. Amsterdam: Veuve de Jacques Desbordes, 1721.

————. *Histoires ou contes du tems passé . . .* Nouvelle Édition augmentée d'une Nouvelle à la fin. Amsterdam: Chez Jacques Desbordes, 1729.

————. *Histories or Tales of Past Times,* Translated into English by Robert Samber. London: J. Pote and R. Montagu, 1729.

————. *Perrault's Popular Tales.* Edited with introducduction by Andrew Lang. Oxford: The Clarendon Press, 1888.

Perrault, Charles. *Perrault's Tales of Mother Goose.* The Dedication Manuscript of 1695. Edited with introduction by Jacques Barchilon. New York: The Pierpont Morgan Library, 1956.

————. *The Fairy Tales of Charles Perrault.* Edited with introduction by Geoffrey Brereton. Edinburgh and Baltimore: Penguin Books, 1957.

Sraparola, Gianfrancesco. *Les Nuictz Facetieuses.* (First translation by Pierre de la Rivey). Paris: Abel Langelier, 1585.

Thurber, James. *Fables for our Times.* New York: Harper's, 1940.

The Literature of Mother Goose

Barnes, Walter. *The Children's Poets.* New York: The World Book Company, 1924.

Halliwell, James Orchard. *The Nursery Rhymes of England,*

Collected principally from oral tradition. London: The Percy Society, 1842.

Meigs, Cornelia (and others). *A Critical History of Children's Literature*. New York: The Macmillan Company, 1953.

Nadeau, John. "Mother Goose Exposed!" *Education,* Volume 80, No. 8 (April, 1960).

Opie, Iona and Peter, eds. *The Oxford Dictionary of Nursery Rhymes*. Oxford: The Clarendon Press, 1951.

Mother Goose's Melody: or, Sonnets for the Cradle . . . London: F. Power, 1791.

Mother Goose's Melody. Worcester, Mass.: Isaiah Thomas, 1794.

Prideaux, W. F. (ed.). *Mother Goose's Melody: A Facsimile Reproduction of the Earliest Known Edition*. London: Bullen, 1904.

Weedon, M. J. P. "Mother Goose's Melody," *The Library*. Fifth Series, Volume VI, No. 3/4 (December, 1951). Oxford: Oxford University Press.

Whitmore, William H. *Mother Goose's Melody,* as issued by John Newberry, of London, *circa* 1760 [1781]; Isaiah Thomas of Worchester, Mass., *circa* 1785, and Munroe and Francis, of Boston, *circa* 1825 . . . To which are added the Fairy Tales of Mother Goose first collected by Perrault. Boston: Damrell and Upham. London: Griffith Farrar and Company, 1892.

Sackville-West, V. *Nursery Rhymes*. London: The Dropmore Press, 1947.

Welsh, Charles. *A Bookseller of the Last Century*. London: Griffith, 1885.

MOTHER GOOSE'S

TALES

Text of the 1729 Perrault Translation

HISTORIES,

OR

TALES of paſt Times :

VIZ.

I. The Little Red Riding-hood.
II. The Fairy.
III. The Blue Beard.
IV. The Sleeping Beauty in the Wood.
V. The Maſter Cat, or Puſs in Boots.
VI. *Cinderilla*, or the Little Glaſs Slipper.
VII. *Riquet a la Houpe*.
VIII. Little *Poucet*, and his Brothers.
IX. The Diſcreet Princeſs, or the Adventures of *Finetta*.

With MORALS.

By M. PERRAULT.

Tranſlated into Engliſh.

LONDON:

Printed for J. POTE, at Sir *Iſaac New-ton's* Head, near *Suffolk-ſtreet, Charing-croſs*; and R. MONTAGU, the Corner of *Great Queen-ſtreet*, near *Drury-lane.* M.DCC.XXIX.

FOREWORD

Very little information about Robert Samber, the translator of Perrault, is available. He was a prolific translator, as the catalog of the British Museum shows. He translated works from Latin, from Italian, and from French.

The text which he used for his translation was the French edition of 1721 or its reprint of 1729 published in Holland. In these, the sequence in the original Perrault edition of 1697 has been changed. "The Little Red Riding Hood" is the first story, then follow "The Fairy," "The Blue Beard," "The Sleeping Beauty in the Wood," "The Master Cat, or Puss in Boots," "Cinderilla, or The Little Glass Slipper," "Riquet à la Houppe," and "Little Poucet and his brothers." Samber translates and presents the stories in this same order, and he also adds the translation of another story from the Dutch editions (not by Perrault, but by Jeanne l'Héritier), "The Discreet Princess, or the Adventures of Finetta."

Samber dedicated his translation to the wife of George Granville, Lord Lansdowne. The countess of Granville, reported to be very handsome, was the daughter of Edmund Villiers. Samber's dedication to her contains an interesting idea about the superiority of French fairy tales over English nursery rhymes. He seems to despise children's writers who "content themselves in Venting some poor insipid trifling Tale in a little tinkling Jingle, adding some petty Witticism, or insignificant useless Reflection, which they call a Moral, and think they have done the Business."

The translation in general is competent. Samber is not to be censured when the language itself is at fault. For instance, he translated the French word *bucheron* by *faggot-maker* when *wood-cutter* would seem preferable; however, *wood-cutter* was not yet in the English vocabulary. Often, though, his translation is too literal and betrays a lack of intimacy with the French language. On other occasions he deliberately departs from the text and adds short digressions. One interpolation (in "Sleeping Beauty") is amusing: Samber felt the need to say this about the nature of ogres, "Now, an ogre is a giant that has long teeth and claws, with a raw head and bloody bones, that runs away with naughty little boys and girls, and eats them up."

The illustrations in the English text which is here reproduced are copies of those in the Dutch editions. They compare favorably with the illustrations in the original French edition and its many copies. Even though Perrault's translation became very popular, in its first edition it survives in only one copy, that owned by Mr. Augustus P. Loring of Boston. Our text is reproduced with kind authorization of its owner from photostats of this copy in the Houghton Library, Harvard University. In the interest of readability, our reproductions are larger than the original. The frontispiece to this foreword is actual size.

HISTORIES,

OR

TALES of paſt Times :

VIZ.

With MORALS.

By M. PERRAULT.

Tranſlated into Engliſh.

LONDON :

Printed for J. POTE, at Sir *Iſaac New-ton's* Head, near *Suffolk-ſtreet*, *Charing-croſs* ; and R. MONTAGU, the Corner of *Great Queen-ſtreet*, near *Drury-lane*. M.DCC.XXIX.

M A D A M,

 Roman *Lady,* *by Way of Oſtentation, ſhewed to Another of her Acquaintance her Jewels; who, in Return, ſhewed her her Children, ſaying,* Thoſe were her Jewels : *And indeed, ſuch are Children, when rendered brillant by a virtuous Education, whereby they may become, in their reſpective Stations, ſerviceable and ornamental to their Country; Stateſmen, Ambaſſadors, Patriots, Vice-Roys. Your Ladyſhip is ſenſibly convinc'd of the Certainty of this Truth, in ſeeing ſo happily ſucceed your*

A 2 *Ma-*

DEDICATION.

Maternal Care in the Perfon of my LORD CARTERET, *who has been fo glorioufly eminent in all thofe great Qualities: and your Ladyfhip moreover fees yourfelf at the Head of a numerous and noble Offspring, which we may hope, through the fame Care and Influence, will fhine in their feveral Spheres, with equal Radiancy and Splendor.*

THIS I prefume here to mention, that you might not, Madam, be furprifed at my Offering to you the following Piece, which, as little and trifling as at firft View it may feem to be, has notwithftanding no little Merit.

I need not trouble your Ladyfhip with a long Account of the Excellency of Inftruction by Fable, which has been fo well approved of, fo highly recommended, and fo fuccefsfully and profitably made ufe of by the greateft Sages in the World, the wifeft and beft of Men in all Ages; there being nothing in the Productions of the Mind.

DEDICATION.

Mind, so delightful and diverting, and at the same time so instructive, as what we meet with in Apologue and Fable, which, childish as its Appearances may sometimes be, carries notwithstanding in the Bottom, a most solid Sense, and wraps up and infolds the most material and important Truths.

THE Divine PLATO *had such a Value and Esteem for this kind of Writing, that he seems to have preferred it to Poetry itself: For though he banished* HOMER *his Commonwealth, he assigned in it a very honourable Post for* ÆSOP. *He desires Children might suck in those Fables with their Milk, and recommends it to Nurses to teach them to 'em, since we cannot accustom our selves too soon to Wisdom and Virtue; and rather than to be reduced to the painful Necessity of correcting our Habits, we ought to strive to make them good, while they are in the State of Indifference.*

BUT

DEDICATION.

BUT however instructive the Stories of Animals may be, it is certain they do not make such strong Impressions on the Mind, nor move the Affections so much as those related of human Kind. Children have been known to weep at the Distress of the two Children in the Wood, who would not be any wise affected with the Adventures of Cocks and Bulls, &c. they knew very well what they of their own species are, but the Natures and Properties of those Creatures we are pleased to call irrational, they are too young to have any tolerable Idea or Notion of.

THE Author of the following Stories has happily succeeded in this Way, and perhaps nothing yet extant can equal them in their admirable Design and Execution. It was however objected, that some of them were very low and childish, especially the first. It is very true, and therein consists their Excellency. They therefore who made this as an Objection, did not

seem

DEDICATION.

seem very well to underſtand what they ſaid; they ſhould have reflected they are deſigned for Children: And yet the Author hath ſo ingeniouſly and maſterly contrived them, that they inſenſibly grow up, gradually one after another, in Strength and Beauty, both as to their Narration and Moral, and are told with ſuch a Naiveté, and natural innocent Simplicity, that not only Children, but thoſe of Maturity, will alſo find in them uncommon Pleaſure and Delight.

THEY were dedicated to no leſs than a Princeſs of the Blood of France, and the famous Perrault *was ſo taken with them, that he made himſelf their Morals, as knowing they tended to the Encouragement of Virtue, and the Depreſſing of Vice: the former of which is ever rewarded in them, and the latter ever puniſhed, the true End and Deſign of Fable; a thing which our Fabuliſts of late ſeem to have the Modeſty not ſo much as to pretend to; they content themſelves in*

Venting

DEDICATION.

Venting some poor insipid trifling Tale in a little tinkling Jingle, adding some petty Witticisms, or insignificant useless Reflection, which they call a Moral, and think they have done the Business. But was PLATO *now alive, he would undoubtedly banish out of his Common-wealth* Æsop *as well as* Homer.

BUT I am afraid, Madam, I have too long tired your Patience, so shall only add, that I hope your Ladyship will be pleased to accept this little Present, and which perhaps may be useful to the Infant Relatives of your Ladyship, as a Mark of the profound Respect, and singular Veneration which our Family retains for that of your Ladyship.

I am with intire submission,

MADAM,

Your Ladyship's most humble,

and

most obedient Servant,

ROBERT SAMBER.

THE

Little red Riding-Hood.

TALE I.

HERE was once upon a time a little country girl, born in a village, the prettiest little creature that ever was seen. her mother was beyond reason excessively fond of her, and her grandmother yet much more. This

B good

good woman caufed to be made for her a little red Riding-Hood; which made her look fo very pretty, that every body call'd her, *The little red Riding-Hood.*

ONE day, her mother having made fome cuftards, faid to her, Go my little *Biddy*, for her chriftian name was *Biddy*, go and fee how your grandmother does, for I hear fhe has been very ill, carry her a cuftard, and this little pot of butter. *The little red Riding-Hood* fets out immediately to go to her grandmother, who lived in another village. As fhe was going through the wood, fhe met with *Goffop Wolfe*, who had a good mind to eat her up, but he did not dare, becaufe of fome faggot-makers that were in the forreft.

HE asked of her whither fhe was going: The poor child, who did not know how dangerous a
thing

thing it is to ſtay and hear a
Wolfe talk, ſaid to him, I am going to ſee my grandmamma, and
carry her a cuſtard pye, and a little pot of butter my mamma ſends
her. Does ſhe live far off? ſaid
the Wolfe. Oh! ay, ſaid *the little red
Riding-Hood,* on the other ſide of
the mill below yonder, at the firſt
houſe in the village. Well, ſaid
the Wolfe, and I'll go and ſee her
too; I'll go this way, and go you
that, and we ſhall ſee who will be
there ſooneſt.

THE Wolfe began to run as faſt
as he was able, the ſhorteſt way;
and the little girl went the longeſt,
diverting her ſelf in gathering nuts,
running after butterflies, and making noſe-gays of all the little flowers ſhe met with. The Wolfe was
not long before he came to the
grandmother's houſe; he knocked
at the door *toc toc.* Whoſe there?
Your grand-daughter, *The little red*

Riding-Hood, faid the Wolfe, coun-
terfeiting her voicè, who has
brought you a cuftard pye, and
a little pot of butter mamma fends
you.

THE good grandmother, who
was in bed, becaufe fhe found
herfelf fomewhat ill, cried out, Pull
the bobbin, and the latch will go
up. The Wolfe pull'd the bobbin, and the door open'd ; upon
which he fell upon the good woman, and eat her up in the tenth
part of a moment; for he had
eaten nothing for above three days
before. After that, he fhut the
door, and went into the grandmother's bed, expecting *the little
red Riding-Hood*, who came fome
time afterwards, and knock'd at
the door *toc toc, Who's there?*
The *Little red Riding-Hood*, who
hearing the big voice of the Wolfe,
was at firft afraid; but believing
her grandmother had got a cold,
and

and was grown hoarfe, faid, it is
your grandaughter, *The little red
Riding-Hood*, who has brought you
a cuftard pye, and a little pot of
butter mamma fends you. The
Wolfe cried out to her, foftening
his voice as much as he could,
Pull the bobbin, and the latch will
go up. The *little red Riding-
Hood* pull'd the bobbin, and the
door opened.

THE Wolfe feeing her come in,
faid to her, hiding himfelf under the
clothes. Put the cuftard, and the
little pot of butter upon the ftool,
and come into bed to me. *The
little red Riding-Hood* undreffed her
felf, and went into bed, where fhe
was very much aftonifhed to fee
how her grandmother looked in her
night-cloaths: So fhe faid to her,
*Grandmamma, what great arms you
have got!* It is the better to embrace thee my pretty child. *Grandmamma, what great legs you have*
B 3 *got.*

got! it is to run the better my
child. *Grandmamma, what great
ears you have got!* It is to hear the
better my child. *Grandmamma, what
great eyes you have got!* It is to see
the better my child. *Grandmamma,
what great teeth you have got!* It
is to eat thee up. And upon saying these words, this wicked
Wolfe fell upon *the little Red Riding-Hood,* and eat her up.

The MORAL.

*FRom this short story easy we
discern
What conduct all young people ought
to learn.
But above all, the growing ladies
fair,
Whose orient rosy Blooms begin t'appear:
Who, Beauties in the fragrant spring
of age!
With pretty airs young hearts are
apt t'engage.*

III

Ill do they listen to all sorts of
   tongues,
Since some enchant and lure like Syrens songs.
No wonder therefore 'tis if over-
   pow'rd,
So many of them has the Wolfe devour'd.
The Wolfe, I say, for Wolves too
   sure there are
Of every sort, and every character.
Some of them mild and gentle-hu-
   mour'd be
Of noise and gall, and rancour
   wholly free;
Who tame, familiar, full of com-
   plaisance;
Ogle and leer, languish, cajole and
   glance;
With luring tongues, and language
   wondrous sweet,
Follow young ladies as they walk
   the street,

B 4   Ev'n

Ev'n to their very houses and bed-
　　ſide,
And though their true deſigns they
　　artful hide,
Yet ah! theſe ſimpring Wolves, who
　　does not ſee
Moſt dang'rous of all Wolves in
　　faſt to be ?

The

The FAIRY.

TALE II.

 HERE was once upon a time a widow, who had two daughters, the eldeſt was ſo much like her in face and hu-mour, that whoever looked upon the daughter ſaw the mother. They were both ſo diſagreeable and ſo proud, that no body could

B 5　　　　live

live with them. The youngeſt who
was the very picture of the father
for civility and ſweetneſs of temper, was withal one of the moſt
beautiful girls that ever was ſeen.
This mother loved even to diſ-
traction her eldeſt daughter, and
at the ſame time had a frightful
averſion for the youngeſt.   She
made her eat in the kitchen and
work continually.

AMONGST other things, this
poor child was forced twice a day
to draw water above a mile and
a half off the houſe, and bring a
pitcher full of it home. ʼOne day
as ſhe was at this fountain there
came up to her a poor woman,
who begged of her to let her drink:
O ay with all my heart, Goody,
ſaid this pretty little girl ; and
rinſing immediately the pitcher,
ſhe took up ſome water from the
cleareſt place of the fountain, and
gave it to her, holding up the pitcher

cher all the while that she might drink the eafier.

THE good woman having drank what she had a mind to, said to her, You are fo very pretty, my dear, fo good and fo mannerly, that I cannot help giving of you a gift (for this was a Fairy, you muft underftand, who had taken upon her the form of a poor countrywoman to fee how far the civility and good manners of this pretty girl would go.) *I will give you for gift* *, continued the fairy, that at every word you fpeak there shall come out of your mouth either a flower or a jewel.

WHEN this pretty girl came home, her mother fcolded at her

* Thefe words the fairies make ufe of when they have a mind to do good or harm to any body.

for

for returning ſo late from the fountain. I beg your pardon, mamma, ſaid the poor thing, for ſtaying ſo long, and immediately upon ſpeaking theſe words there came out of her mouth two ro-ſes, two pearls, and two large di-amonds. What is it I ſee there, ſaid her mother all aſtoniſhed, I think I ſee pearls and diamonds come out of her mouth : How comes this, child? (This was the firſt time ſhe ever call'd her child.) The poor creature told her plainly all that had happen'd, not without dropping out of her mouth an infinite number of di-amonds. Truly, ſaid the mother, I muſt ſend thither my daughter. Come hither, *Fanny*, ſee what comes out of your ſiſter's mouth when ſhe ſpeaks : Wou'd not you be glad to have the ſame gift gi-ven to you? You have nothing elſe to do but go and draw water out

of

of the fountain, and when a certain poor woman comes to ask to drink a little, to give it her very civilly. It wou'd be a very pretty fight indeed, faid this brute, to fee me go to draw water: I will have you go, faid the mother. So fhe went, but grumbled all the way, taking along with her the beft filver tankard they had in the houfe. She was no fooner at the fountain than fhe faw coming out of the wood a lady moft richly dreft, who came up to her and asked to drink. Now you muft know, that this was the very fairy that appeared to her fifter, but had now taken upon her the air and drefs of a Princefs, to fee how far the rudenefs and ill manners of this girl would go. Am I come hither, faid the proud brute, for nothing elfe but to give you to drink? I have juft now brought a filver tankard on purpofe

4

pose for my lady. You may drink out of it, I think, if you will.

You have not a grain of civility or good breeding in you, reply'd the Fairy, without putting herself into a passion: Well then, since you have so little manners and are so disobliging, *I give you for gift,* that at every word you speak there shall come out of your mouth a snake or a toad. As soon as her mother saw her coming she cry'd out, Well, daughter; Well, mother, answer'd the brute, and at the same time there came out of her mouth two snakes and two toads. O, mercy! cry'd the mother, what is it I see! It is her sister that has been the cause of all this; but she shall pay for it; and immediately she ran after her to beat her. The poor creature fled away from her and

went

went to hide herfelf in the foreft
that was hard by.

THE King's fon, who was returning from hunting, met her,
and feeing her fo very pretty, asked her what fhe did there alone,
and why fhe cry'd! *Alack-a-day !
Sir, my mamma has turned me out
of doors.* The King's fon, who
faw five or fix pearls and as many diamonds come out of her
mouth, defired her to tell him
whence this happen'd. She accordingly told him the whole ftory ; upon which the King's fon fell in love
with her; and confidering with himfelf that fuch a gift as this was
worth more than any marriage portion whatfoever in another, conducted her to the palace of the King his
father, and there married her. As
for her fifter, fhe made herfelf fo
odious that her own mother turn'd
her out of doors, and the unhappy
wretch

wretch having wandered about a
good while without finding any body to take her in, went to a corner
of a wood and died.

The M O R A L.

*M*Oney and jewels *ſtill we find*
    Stamp ſtrong impreſſions on
        the Mind ;
However, ſweet diſcourſe does yet
    much more,
Of greater value is, and greater pow'r.

A N O T H E R.

*C*Ivil behaviour coſts indeed ſome
    pains,
    Requires of complaiſance ſome little
        ſhare ;
But ſoon or late its due reward it
    gains,
    And meets it often when we're not
        aware.

THE

THE

BLUE BEARD.

TALE III.

HERE was once upon a time a man who had feveral fine houfes both in town and country, a good deal of filver and gold plate, embroider'd furniture, and coaches gilt all over

with

with gold. But this fame man had the misfortune to have a *Blue Beard,* which made him fo frightfully ugly that all the women and girls ran away from him.

ONE of his neighbours, a lady of quality, had two daughters who were perfect beauties. He defired of her one of them in marriage, leaving to her the choice of which of them fhe would beftow upon him. They would neither of them have him, and fent him backwards and forwards from one another, being refolved never to marry a man that had a *Blue Beard.* That which moreover gave them the greater difguft and averfion, was that he had already been marry'd to feveral wives, and no body ever knew what were become of them.

THE *Blue Beard*, to engage their affection, took them with my
lady

lady their mother, and three or
four other ladies of their acquaintance, and some young people
of the neighbourhood, to one of
his country 'eats, where they
staid full eight days. There was
nothing now to be seen but parties
of pleasure, hunting of all kinds,
fishing, dancing, feasts and col-
lations. No body went to bed,
they past the night in rallying and
playing upon one another: In short,
every thing so well succeeded, that
the youngest daughter began to
think, that the master of the
house had not a *Beard* so very
Blue, and that he was a very civil gentleman.

ASSOON as they returned home
the marriage was concluded. A-
bout a month afterwards *the Blue
Beard* told his wife, that he was
obliged to take a journey into a
distant country for six weeks at
least, about an affair of very great
con-

confequence, defiring her to divert herfelf in his abfence, fend for her friends and acquaintance, carry them into the country, if fhe pleafed, and make good cheer wherever fhe was : Here, faid he, are the keys of the two great rooms that hold my beft and richeft furniture; thefe are of my filver and gold plate, which is not to be made ufe of every day; thefe open my ftrong boxes, which hold my gold and filver money; thefe my caskets of jewels; and this is the mafter-key that opens all my apartments : But for this little one here, it is the key of the clofet at the end of the great gallery on the ground floor. Open them all, go into all and every one except that little clofet, which I forbid you, and forbid you in fuch a manner, that if you happen to open it, there is nothing but what you may expect from my juft anger and refentment. She
                              promifed

promifed to obferve every thing he
order'd her, who, after having embraced her, got into his coach and
proceeded on his journey.

HER neighbours and good
friends did not ftay to be fent
for by the new married lady, fo
great was their impatience to fee
all the rich furniture of her houfe,
not daring to come while the huf-
band was there, becaufe of his *Blue
Beard* which frighten'd them. They
ran through all the rooms, clofets,
wardrobes, which were all fo rich
and fine that they feemed to fur-
pafs one another. After that, they
went up into the two great rooms
where were the beft and richeft
furniture; they could not fuffi-
ciently admire the number and
beauty of the tapeftry, beds,
couches, cabinets, ftands, tables
and looking-glaffes, in which you
might fee yourfelf from head to
fot ; fome of them were framed
with

with glaſs, others with ſilver and
ſilver gilt, the fineſt and moſt magnificent as ever were ſeen: They
never ceaſed to extol and envy the
happineſs of their friend, who in
the mean time no ways diverted
herſelf in looking upon all theſe
rich things, becauſe of the impatience ſhe had to go and open the
cloſet of the ground floor. She
was ſo much preſſed by her curi-
oſity, that without conſidering that
it was very uncivil to leave her
company, ſhe went down a back
pair of ſtairs, and with ſuch an exceſſive haſte, that ſhe had like to
have broken her neck two or three
times.

BEING come to the cloſet door,
ſhe ſtopt for ſome time, thinking
upon her husband's orders, and
conſidering what unhappineſs might
attend her were ſhe diſobedient;
but the temptation was ſo ſtrong
ſhe could not overcome it: She
took

took then the little key and opened it in a very great trembling.
But she could see nothing diftinctly,
becaufe the windows were fhut ; after fome moments fhe began to obferve that the floor was all co-
vered over with clotted blood, on
which lay the bodies of feveral
dead women ranged againft the
walls. (Thefe were all the wives
that the *Blue Beard* had married
and murder'd one after another.)
She thought that fhe fhould have
died for fear, and the key that
fhe pulled out of the lock fell out
of her hand : After having fomewhat recover'd her furprife, fhe
took up the key, locked the door
and went up ftairs into her chamber to recover herfelf, but fhe
could not, fo much was fhe frightened. Having obferved that the
key of the clofet was ftain'd with
blood, fhe tried two or three times
to wipe it off, but the blood would
not come out; in vain did fhe wafh

it

it and even rub it with foap and
fand, the blood ftill remained, for
the key was a Fairy, and fhe could
never quite make it clean; when
the blood was gone off from one
fide, it came again on the other.

THE *Blue Beard* returned from
his journey the fame evening, and
faid he had received letters upon
the road, informing him that the
affair he went about was finifhed
to his advantage. His wife did
all fhe could to convince him fhe
was extremely glad of his fpeedy
return. The next morning he
asked for the keys, which fhe returned, but with fuch a trembling
hand, that he cafily guefs'd what
had happen'd. What is the matter, faid he, that the key of the
clofet is not amongft the reft? I
muft certainly, faid fhe, have left
it above upon the table. Do not
fail, faid the *Blue Beard*, of giving it to me prefently: After feveral
goings

goings backwards and forwards she was forced to bring him the key. The *Blue Beard* having very attentively confider'd it, faid to his Wife, how comes this blood upon the key? I don't know, faid the poor Woman paler than death. You don't know, replied the *Blue Beard*, I know very well, you were refolv'd to go into the clofet, were you not? Very well, Madam, you fhall go in, and take your place amongft the ladies you faw there.

Upon this fhe threw herfelf at her husband's feet, and begged his pardon with all the figns of a true repentance, and that fhe would never more be difobedient. She would have melted a rock, fo beautiful and forrowful was fhe; but the *Blue Beard* had a heart harder than the hardeft rock! You muft die, Madam, faid he, and that prefently. Since I muft die, faid fhe, looking upon him with

C   her

her eyes all bathed in tears, give me some little time to say my prayers. I give you, said the *Blue Beard*, a quarter of an hour, but not one moment more.

WHEN she was alone, she called out to her sister, and said to her, Sister *Anne*, for that was her name, go up, I desire thee, upon the top of the tower, and see if my brothers are not coming, they promised me that they would come to day, and if thou seest them, give them a sign to make haste. Her sister *Anne* went up upon the top of the tower, and the poor afflicted lady cried out from time to time, *Anne, sister Anne, dost thou see nothing coming?* And sister *Anne* said, *I see nothing but the sun that makes a dust, and the grass that grows green.* In the mean while the *Blue Beard*, holding a great cutlass in his hand, cried out as loud as he could to his wife, Come down presently,

or

or I'll come up to you. One moment longer, if you pleafe, faid
his wife, and immediately fhe cried
out very foftly, *Anne, fifter Anne,
doft thou fee nothing coming?* And
fifter *Anne* faid, *I fee nothing but
the fun that makes a duft, and the
grafs that grows green.* Come
down quickly, cried the *Blue Beard*,
or I'll come up to you. I am
coming, anfwer'd his wife, and
then fhe cried, *Anne, fifter Anne, doft
thou fee nothing coming?* I fee, replied fifter *Anne*, a great duft that
comes on this fide here. *Are they
my brothers?* Alas! no, my dear
fifter, I fee a flock of fheep. Will
you not come down? cried the
Blue Beard. One moment longer,
faid his wife, and then fhe cried
out, *Anne, fifter Anne, doft thou fee
nothing coming?* I fee, faid fhe, two
horfemen coming, but they are yet
a great way off. God be praifed,
faid fhe immediately after, they
are my brothers.; I have made
C 2　　　　them

them a fign as well as I can to make hafte. The *Blue Beard* cried out now fo loud, that he made the whole houfe tremble.

THE poor Lady came down and threw herfelf at his feet all in tears with her hair about her fhoulders: This fignifies nothing, fays the *Blue Beard*, you muft die; then taking hold of her hair with one hand, and holding up the cutlafs with the other, he was going to cut off her head. The poor lady turning about to him, and looking at him with dying eyes, defired him to afford her one little moment to recollect herfelf : No, no, faid he, recommend thy felf to God: for at this very inftant there was fuch a loud knocking at the gate, that the *Blue Beard* ftopt fhort of a fudden: They open'd the gate, and immediately enter'd two horfemen, who drawing their fwords, ran directly

to

to the *Blue Beard.* He knew them
to be his wife's brothers, one a dra-
goon, the other a mulqueteer, ſo
that he ran away immediately to
ſave himſelf: but the two brothers
purſued him ſo cloſe, that they
overtook him before he could get
to the ſteps of the porch, when
they ran their ſwords through his
body and left him dead.

THE poor lady was almoſt as
dead as her husband, and had not
ſtrength enough to riſe and embrace her brothers. The *Blue
Beard* had no heirs, and ſo his
wife became miſtreſs of all his e-
ſtate. She made uſe of one part of
it to marry her ſiſter *Anne* to a
young gentleman who had loved
her a long while, another part to
buy captains commiſſions for her
brothers, and the reſt to marry
herſelf to a very honeſt gentleman,
who made her forget the ill time
ſhe had paſs'd with the *Blue Beard.*
C 3   The

The MORAL.

O Curiosity, thou mortal bane!
  Spite of thy charms, thou causest
often pain
And sore, regret, of which we daily
  find
A thousand instances attend man-
  kind:
For thou, O may it not displease the
  fair,
A flitting pleasure art, but lasting
  care;
And always costs, alas! too dear the
  prize,
Which, in the moment of possession,
  dies.

ANOTHER.

A Very little share of common
  sense
And knowledge of the world, will
  soon evince,

That

That this a ſtory is of time long paſt,
No huſbands now ſuch panick terrors
   caſt;
Nor weakly, with a vain deſpotick
   band,
Imperious, what's impoſſible, com-
   mand:
And be they diſcontented, or the fire
Of wicked jealouſy their hearts in-
   ſpire,
They ſoftly ſing; and of whatever
   hue
Their beards may chance to be, or
   black, or blue,
Grizzled, or ruſſet, it is hard to ſay
Which of the two, the man or wife,
   bears ſway.

THE

SLEEPING BEAUTY
in the WOOD.

TALE IV.

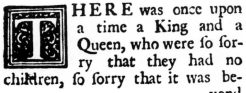

THERE was once upon a time a King and a Queen, who were fo forry that they had no children, fo forry that it was beyond
yond

yond expreffion. They went to all
the waters in the world, vows,
pilgrimages, every thing was tried
and nothing came of it. At laft
however the Queen was with child;
and was brought to bed of a daughter: There was a very fine Chriftening; and the Princefs had for
her godmothers all the Fairies they
could find in the kingdom (of
whom they found feven) that every one of them might give her a
gift, as was the cuftom of Fairies
in thofe days; by this means the
Princefs had all the perfections
imaginable.

AFTER the ceremonies of the
Chriftening were over, all the company return'd to the King's palace, where there was prepared a
great feaft for the Fairies. There
was placed before every one of
them a magnificent cover with a
cafe of maffive gold, wherein was a
fpoon, knife and fork, all of pure

C 5   gold

gold set with diamonds and rubies.
But as they were all sitting down
to dinner, they saw come into the
hall an old Fairy, whom they had
not invited, because it was now
above fifty years since she had been
seen out of a tower, and they
thought her either dead or enchanted. The King order'd her a cover,
but could no give her a case of
gold as the others, because they
had seven only made for the seven
Fairies. The old Fairy fancied
she was slighted, and mutter'd some
threats between her teeth. One
of the young Fairies, who sat by
her, heard her, and judging that
she might give the little Princess
some unhappy gift, went as soon
as they rose from table and hid
herself behind the hangings, that
she might speak last, and repair as
much as possibly she could the e-
vil that the old Fairy might do
her.

IN

IN the mean while all the Fairies began to give their gifts to the Princess. The youngest gave her for gift that she should be the most beautiful person in the world; the next, that she should have the wit of an angel; the third, that she should have an admirable grace in every thing she did; the fourth, that she should dance perfectly well; the fifth, that she should sing like a nightingale; and the sixth, that she should play upon all kinds of musick to the utmost perfection.

THE old Fairy's turn coming next, with a head shaking more with spite than old age, she said, that the Princess should have her hand pierced with a spindle and die of the wound. This terrible gift made the whole company tremble, and every body fell a crying.

AT

AT this very inftant the young
Fairy came out from behind the
hangings, and fpoke thefe words
aloud: Affure yourfelves, O King
and Queen, that your daughter
fhall not die of this difafter : It is
true, I have not power to undo intirely what my Ancient has done.
The Princefs fhall indeed pierce
her hand with a fpindle ; but inftead of dying, fhe fhall only fall
into a profound fleep which fhall
laft a hundred years, at the expiration of which a King's fon fhall
come and awake her.

THE King, to avoid the misfortune foretold by the old Fairy,
caufed immediately proclamation
to be made, whereby every body
was forbidden on pain of death
to fpin with a diftaff and fpindle,
or to have fo much as any fpindle
in their houfes. About fifteen or
fixteen years after, the King and
Queen

Queen being gone to one of their houses of pleafure, the young Princefs happen'd one day to divert herfelf in running up and down the palace, when going up from one apartment to another, fhe came into a little room on the top of the great tower, where a good old woman was fpinning with her fpindle. This good woman had never heard of the King's proclamation againft fpindles. What are you doing there, faid the Princefs? I am fpinning, my pretty child, faid the old woman, who did not know who fhe was. Ha! faid the Princefs, this is very pretty, how do you do it? Give it to me, that I may fee if I can do fo : She had no fooner taken it into her hand, than, whether being very hafty at it, fomewhat unhandy, or that the decree of the Fairy had fo ordained it, it ran into her hand, and fhe fell down in a fwoon.

THE

THE good old woman not knowing very well what to do in this affair, cried out for help : People came in from every quarter in great numbers, they threw water upon the Princess's face, unlaced her, struck her on the palms of her hands, and rubbed her temples with *Hungary-water*; but nothing would bring her to herself.

AND now the King, who came up at the noise, bethought himself of the prediction of the Fairies, and judging very well that this must necessarily come to pass since the Fairies had said it, caused the Princess to be carried into the finest apartment in the palace, and to be laid upon a bed all embroider'd with gold and silver ; one would have taken her for a little Angel, she was so very beautiful ; for her swooning away had not diminished one bit of her complexion ;
her

her checks were carnation, and her lips like coral : She had only her eyes fhut, but they heard her breathe foftly, which fatisfied them that fhe was not dead. The King commanded that they fhould not difturb her, but let her fleep quietly till her hour of awaking was come.

THE good Fairy, who had faved her life by condemning her to fleep an hundred years, was in the kingdom of *Matakin* twelve thoufand leagues off, when this accident befel the Princefs; but fhe was inform'd of it in an inftant by a little dwarf, who had boots of feven leagues, that is, boots with which he could tread over feven leagues of ground at one ftride. The Fairy came away immediately, and 'fhe arrived about an hour after in a fiery chariot, drawn by dragons. The King handed her out of the chariot, and fhe approved every thing he had done; but as fhe had

a very

a very great forefight, fhe thought
when the Princefs fhould awake fhe
might not know what to do with
herfelf, being all alone in this old
palace; and this was what fhe did.
She touched with her wand every
thing that was in the palace (except the King and the Queen) go-
vernefles, maids of honour, ladies
of the bed-chamber, gentlemen,
officers, ftewards, cooks, under-
cooks, fcullions, guards with their
beef-eaters, pages, footmen; fhe
likewife touch'd all the horfes that
were in the ftables, as well pads as
others, the great dogs in the outward court, and pretty little *Mopfey*
too the Princefs's little Spaniel
bitch that lay by her on the bed.

IMMEDIATELY upon her touching them they all fell afleep, that
they might not awake before their
miftrefs, and that they might be
ready to wait upon her when fhe
wanted them. The very fpits at
the

the fire, as full as they could hold
of partridges and pheafants, alfo
flept. All this was done in a moment ; the Fairies are not long in
doing their bufinefs.

AND now the King and the
Queen having kiffed their dear child
without waking her, went out of
the palace, and put forth a proclamation, that no body fhould dare
to come near it. This however
was not neceffary ; for in a quarter
of an hour's time, there grew up
all round about the park, fuch a
vaft number of trees, great and
fmall, bufhes and brambles twining
one within another, that neither
man nor beaft could pafs through:
fo that they could fee nothing but
the very top of the towers of the
palace and that too, not unlefs it
were a good way off. No body
doubted but the fairy fhewed
herein an extraordinary piece of
her art, that the princefs, while
fhe

she slept, might have nothing to fear from the Curious.

AT the expiration of the hundred years, the son of the King then reigning, and who was of another family from that of the sleeping Princess, being gone a hunting on that side of the country, asked what those towers were that he saw in the middle of a great thick wood: Every one answered according as they had heard. Some said, that it was an old castle haunted by spirits; others, that all the sorcerers and witches of the country kept there their Sabbath, or weekly meeting. The most common opinion was, that an *Ogre* liv'd there, and that he carry'd thither all the little children he could catch hold of, that he might eat them up at his leisure, without any body's being able to follow him, as having himself only the power to pass through the wood.

Now

Now an *Ogre* is a giant that has long teeth. and claws, with a raw head and bloody bones, that runs away with naughty little boys and girls, and eats them up.

THE Prince was in a brown ftudy, not knowing what to believe, when an old conntry-man fpoke to him after this manner. May it pleafe your Royal Highnefs, it is now above fifty years fince I heard my father fay, who heard my grandfather fay, that there then was in this caftle a Princefs, the moft beautiful that ever was feen, that fhe muft fleep there an hundred years, and fhould be waked by a King's fon, for whom fhe was referved. The young Prince was all on fire at thefe words; and believing, without weighing the matter, that he could put an end to this fine adventure, and pufhed on by love and honour, refolv'd that moment to look into it.

SCARCE

SCARCE had he advanced towards the wood, when all the great trees, the bushes and brambles gave way of themselves to let him pass through: he walked up to the castle that he saw at the end of a large Avenue which he went into; and what a little surprized him, was, that he saw none of his people could follow him, because the trees closed again, as soon as he had passed through them. However, he did not cease from continuing his way: a young and amorous Prince is always valiant. He came into an outward court, where every thing he saw might have frozen up the most fearless person with horrour; there reigned all over a most frightful silence; the image of death every where shewed it self, and there was nothing to be seen but stretch'd out bodies of men and animals, that appear'd as if they were dead. He knew

knew however very well, by the ruby
faces and pimpled nofes of the
beef-eaters, that they were only
afleep; and their goblets, wherein ftill remained fome drops of
wine, fhewed plainly, that they
fell afleep in their cups.

HE then croffed a court pav'd
with marble, went up the ftairs, and
came into the guard chamber,
where the guards were ftanding in
their ranks, with their muskets upon
their fhoulders, and fnoring as loud
as they could. After that, he
went through feveral rooms full of
gentlemen and ladies, all afleep,
fome ftanding, others fiting. At
laft, he came into a chamber all
gilt with gold, where he faw upon
a bed, the curtains of which were
all open, the fineft fight that ever
was feen, a Princefs, that appear'd
to be about fifteen or fixteen years
of age, and whofe bright refplen-
dent beauty had fomewhat in it
lumi-

luminous and divine. He approached with trembling and admiration, and fell down before her upon his knees.

AND now, as the enchantment was at an end, the Princeſs awaked, and looking on him with eyes more tender than the firſt view might seem to admit of; is it you my Prince, said ſhe to him, you have waited a great while.

THE Prince charm'd with theſe words, and much more with the manner they were ſpoken in, knew not how to ſhew his joy and gratitude; he aſſured her that he lov'd her better than he did himſelf. Their diſcourſe was not well connected, they wept more than they ſpoke, little eloquence, a great deal of love. He was more at a loſs than ſhe, and we need not wonder at it; ſhe had time to think on what to ſay to him; for
it

it is very probable, (tho' hiſtory mentions nothing of it) that the good fairy, during ſo long a ſleep, had given her very agreeable dreams. In ſhort, they talked four hours together, and yet they did not ſay half the things they had to ſay.

IN the mean while, all the palace awaked; every one thought upon their particular buſineſs; and as all of them were not in love, they were ready to die for hunger: the ladies of honour being as ſharp ſet as other people, grew very impatient, and told the Princeſs aloud, that ſupper was ſerv'd up. The Prince helped the Princeſs to riſe, ſhe was intirely dreſs'd, and very magnificently, but they took care not to tell her, that ſhe was dreſt like my great grandmother, and had a point band peeping over a high collar; ſhe looked not a bit the leſs beautiful and

charm-

charming for all that. They went into the great hall of looking-glasses, where they supped, and were served by the Princess's officers; the violins and hautboys played old tunes, but very excellent, tho' it was now above a hundred years since they had played ; and after supper, without losing any time, the Lord Almoner married them in the chapel of the castle, and the chief lady of honour drew the curtains; they slept very little ; the Princess had no occasion, and the Prince left her the next morning to return into the city, where his father must needs have been in pain for him: the prince told him, that he lost his way in the forrest as he was hunting, and that he had lain at a collier's cottage, who gave him cheese and brown bread.

The King his father, who was a good man, believed him ; but his mother could not be persuaded

this

this was true; and feeing that he
went almoft every day a hunting,
and that he always had an excufe
ready for fo doing, though he had
lain out three or four nights together, fhe began to fufpect he had
fome little amour, for he lived with
the Princefs above two whole years,
and had by her two children, the
eldeft of which, who was a daughter, was named *Morning*, and the
youngeft, who was a fon, they called *Day*, becaufe he was a great
deal more handfome and beautiful
than his fifter. The Queen fpoke
feveral times to her fon, to inform
herfelf after what manner he paft his
life, and that in this he ought in
duty to fatisfy her : but he never
dared to truft her with his fecret, he
feared her though he loved her,
for fhe was of the race of the
Ogres, and the King would never
have married her, had it not been
for her vaft riches; it was even
whifpered about the court, that
D fhe

she had *Ogreish* inclinations ; and that when she saw little children passing by, she had all the difficulty in the world to refrain falling upon them : And so the Prince would never tell her one word.

But when the King was dead, which happened about two years afterward, and he saw himself lord and master, he declared publickly his marriage ; he went in great ceremony to conduct his Queen to the palace. They made a magnificent entry into the capital city, into which she rode between her two children.

Some time after, the King went to make war with the Emperor *Cantalabutte* his neighbour. He left the government of the kingdom to the Queen his mother, and earnestly recommended to her care his wife and children. He was obliged to continue his expedition all the summer

mer, and alſoon as he departed, the Queen-mother ſent her daughter in law and her children to a country houſe in the woods, that ſhe might with the greater caſe put in execution her horrible deſires. Some few days afterwards ſhe went thither her ſelf, and ſaid to her clerk of the kitchen, I have a mind to eat little *Morning* for my dinner to morrow. Ah! Madam, ſaid the clerk of the kitchen! I will have it ſo, ſaid the Queen (and this ſhe ſpoke in the tone of an *Ogreſſe*, who had a ſtrong deſire to eat freſh meat) and I will eat her * with *Sauce Robert*. The poor man knowing very well that he muſt not play tricks with an *Ogreſſe*, took his great knife, and went up into little *Morning*'s chamber: ſhe was then four years old,

* *Sauce Robert* is a *French* ſauce, made with onions ſhred, and boiled tender in butter, to which is added, vinegar, muſtard, ſalt, pepper, and a little wine.

and

and came up to him jumping and luaghing to take him about the neck, and ask him for some sugar candy. Upon which he began to weep, the great knife fell out of his hands, and he went into the back yard, and killed a little lamb, and dress'd it with such good Sauce, that his mistress assured him she had never eaten any thing so good in her life. He had at the same time taken up little *Morning,* and carried her to his wife, to conceal her in the lodging · he had at the bottom of the Court-yard.

About eight days afterwards, the wicked Queen said to the clerk of the kitchen, I'll sup upon little *Day*: he answered not a word, being resolved to cheat her, as he had done before ; he went to find out little *Day*, and saw him with a little file in his hand, with which he was fencing with a great monkey ;

he

he was then only three years of
age, he took him up in his arms,
and carried him to his wife, that
she might conceal him in his lodging along with his sister, and
drest in the room of little *Day* a
young kid very tender, which the
Ogress found to be wonderfully good.

THIS was very well hitherto;
but one evening this wicked Queen
said to the clerk of the kitchen,
I'll eat the Queen with the same
sauce as I had with her children.
It was now that the poor clerk of the
kitchen despaired of being able to
deceive her. The young Queen
was past twenty, not reckoning
the hundred years that she had
slept : her skin was somewhat hard,
though fair and white; and how
to find in the yard a beast so firm,
was what puzzled him: he took
then a resolution, that he might
save his own life, to cut the
Queen's throat; and going up into
her

her chamber with intent to do it at once, he put himſelf into as great a fury as he could poſſibly, and came into the young Queen's chamber with his dagger in his hand, he would not however ſurprize her, but told her, with a great deal of reſpect, the orders he had received from the Queen-mother. Do it, do it, ſaid ſhe, holding out her neck as white as ſnow or alabaſter, execute your orders, and then I ſhall go and ſee my children, my poor children, whom I ſo much and ſo tenderly loved: for ſhe thought them dead ever ſince they had been taken away without her knowledge. No, no, Madam, ſaid the poor clerk of the kitchen, all in tears, you ſhall not die, and yet you ſhall ſee your children again, but then you muſt go home with me to my lodgings, where I have conceal'd them, and I ſhall deceive the Queen once more, by giving her in your ſtead a young hind.

hind. Upon which he conducted
her immediately to his chamber;
where leaving her to embrace her
children, and cry along with them,
he went and dress'd a hind, which
the Queen had for her supper, and
devoured it with the same appetite,
as if it had been the young Queen:
she was very well pleas'd with her
cruelty, and she had 'invented a
story to tell the King at his return, how the mad wolves had
eaten up the Queen his wife, and
her two children.

ONE evening, as she was, according to her custom, rambling round
about the courts, and palace-yards,
to see if she could smell any fresh
meat; she heard in a ground room
little *Day* a crying, for his *Mama*
was going to whip him, because
he had been very naughty, and
she heard at the same time little
Morning begging pardon for her
brother, telling her *Mama*, he
D 4   would

would be good, and would never
do so any more. The *Ogresse* knew
presently the voice of the Queen
and her children, and being quite
mad that she had been thus de-
ceived, she commanded next morning, by break of day, with a
most horrible voice, which made
every body tremble, that they
should bring into the middle of the
great court, a large tub, which she
caused to be filled with toads, vi-
pers, snakes, and all kind of ser-
pents, in order to have thrown
into it the Queen and her children,
the clerk of the kitchen, his wife
and maid; who she had 'given orders should be all brought thither
with their hands tied behind them.
They came accordingly, and the
executioners were just going to
throw them into the tub, when
the King, whom they did not expect so soon, enter'd the court on
horseback; for he came post, and
asked with the utmost astonish-
mcn ,

ment, what that horrible fpectacle meant? No one dared to tell him, when the *Ogreſſe*, all enraged to fee what had happen'd, threw her felf head foremoft into the tub, and was devoured in an inftant by the ugly creatures fhe had ordered to be thrown into it for others. He could not but be very forry, for fhe was his mother, but he foon comforted himfelf with his beautiful wife, and his pretty children.

The MORAL.

I.

TO get a husband rich, genteel and gay,
Of humour sweet, some time to stay,
Is natural enough, 'tis true.
But then to wait an hundred years,
And all that while asleep, appears
A thing intirely new.
Now at this time of day,

Not onc of all the fex we fee
To fleep with fuch profound tran-
quillity.

II.

But yet this Fable feems to let us know
That very often Hymen's bliffes fweet,
Altho' fome tedious obftacles they meet,
Which make us for them a long
while to ftay,
Are not lefs happy for approaching
flow :
And that we nothing lofe by fuch
delay.

III.

But warm'd by nature's lambent fires,
The fex fo ardently afpires
Of this blefs'd ftate the facred joy
t'embrace,
And with fuch earneft heart purfus
'em :
I've not the will, I muft confefs,
Nor yet the power, nor fine addrefs,
To preach this moral to 'em.

THE

THE
MASTER CAT:
Or PUSS in BOOTS.
TALE V.

 HERE was once upon a time a Miller, who left no more eſtate to the three children that he had, who were all boys, but his mill, his aſs, and his Cat. The partition was ſoon made. Neither

ther the fcrivener nor attorney were
fent for; they would foon have
eaten up all the poor patrimony.
The eldeft had the mill, the fecond the afs, and the youngeft
nothing but the Cat.

THE poor young fellow was
quite comfortlefs at having fo poor
a lot. My brothers, faid he, may
get their living very handfomly, by
joyning their ftocks together; but
for my part, when I have eaten up
my Cat, and made me a muff of
his skin, I muft die with hunger.
The Cat, who heard all this, but
made as if he did not, faid to him
with a grave and ferious air, Do
not thus afflict your felf, my good
mafter, you have nothing elfe to do,
but to give me a bag, and get
a pair of boots made for me, that
I may fcamper through the dirt
and the brambles, and you fhall fee
that you have not fo bad a portion
of me as you imagine.

THOUGH

THOUGH the Cat's mafter did not build very much upon what he faid, he had often however feen him play a great many cunning tricks to catch rats and mice; as when he ufed to hang by his feet, or hide himfelf in the meal, and make as if he was dead; fo that he did not altogether defpair of his affording him fome help in his miferable condition. When the Cat had what he asked for, he booted himfelf very gallantly; and putting his bag about his neck, he held the two ftrings of it in his two fore-paws, and went into a warren where there was a great number of rabbits. He put bran and fowthiftle into his bag, and ftretching himfelf out at length, as if he had been dead, he waited for fome young rabbits, not yet acquainted with the deceits of the world, to come and rummage his bag for what he had put into it.

SCARCE

SCARCE was he lain down, but
he had what he wanted ; a filly
rash young rabbit jumped into his
bag, and Mr. Puſs drawing immediately the ſtrings, took him
and killed him without mercy.
Proud of his prey, he went with
it to the palace, and asked to ſpeak
with the King. He was ſhewed
up ſtairs into his Majeſty's apartment, and ſaid to him, I have
brought you, Sir, a rabbit of the
warren which my maſter, my lord
marquiſs of *Carabas* (for that was
the title he was pleaſed to give
his maſter) has commanded me to
make your Honour a Preſent of
from him. Tell thy maſter, ſaid
the King, that I thank him, and
he does me a great deal of pleaſure.

ANOTHER time he went and
hid himſelf amongſt the corn, holding ſtill his bag open ; and when
4   he

he saw a brace of partridges run into it, he drew the strings, and took them. He went and made a present of these to the King, as he had done before of the rabbit. The King in like manner received the partridges with a great deal of pleasure, and ordered him some money to drink. The Cat continued after this manner for two or three months, to carry, from time to time, game of his master's taking to the King. One day above the rest, when he knew for certain that he was to take the air along the river side with his daughter, the most beautiful Princess in the world, he said to his master, if you will follow my advice, your fortune is made: you have nothing else to do, but go and wash yourself in the river, in that part I shall shew you, and leave the rest to me. The marquiss of *Carabas* did what the Cat advised him to, without knowing why or wherefore.

WHILE

WHILE he was washing, the King passed by, and the Cat began to cry out as loud as he could, Help, help, my Lord Marquifs of *Carabas* is going to be drown'd. At this noife the King put his head out of the window of his coach, and finding it was the Cat who had brought him so often so much good game, he commanded his guards to run immediately to the affiftance of the Marquifs of *Carabas*.

WHILE they were drawing the poor Marquifs out of the river, the Cat came up to the coach, and told the King, that while his mafter was washing, there came by fome robbers, who went off with his clothes, though he had cried out thieves feveral times, as loud as he could: this cunning rogue of a Cat had hidden them under a great ftone. The King immediately commanded the officers

cers of his wardrobe to go and
fetch one of his beft fuits of
clothes for the Lord Marquifs of
Carabas. The King carefled him
after a very extraordinary manner;
and as the fine clothes he had given
him fet off his good mien (for he
was well made, and very handfome
in his perfon) the King's daughter
took a fecret inclination to him,
and the Marquifs of *Carabas* had
no fooner caft two or three refpect-
ful and fomewhat tender glances,
but fhe fell in love with him to
diftraction. The King made him
to come into the coach, and take
part of the airing. The Cat, quite
ravifhed to fee his defign fucceed,
marched on before, and meeting
with fome countrymen, who were
mowing a meadow, he faid to
them, *Good people, you that mow,
if you do not tell the King, that the
meadow you mow belongs to my Lord
Marquifs of* Carabas, *you fhall be*
cbop-

chopped as ſmall as herbs for the
pot.

THE King did not fail asking
of the mowers, whom the meadow
they were mowing belong'd to ; to
my Lord Marquiſs of *Carabas,*
ſaid they all together ; for the
Cat's threats had made them terribly afraid. You ſee, Sir, ſaid the
Marquiſs, this is a meadow which
never fails to yield a plentiful har-
veſt every year. The Maſter-Cat,
who went ſtill on before, met with
ſome reapers, and ſaid to them,
*Good people, you that reap, if you
do not tell the King, that all this
corn belongs to the Lord Marquiſs of*
Carabas, *you ſhall be chopped as
ſmall as herbs for the pot.*

THE King, who paſſed by a moment after, would know whom all
that corn which he then ſaw belong'd to ; to my Lord Marquiſs of
Carabas, ſaid the reapers, and the
King

King was very well pleafed with it, as well as the Marquifs. whom he congratulated thereupon. The Mafter-Cat, who went always before, faid the fame words to all that he met: and the King was aftonifhed at the vaft eftates of my Lord Marquifs of *Carabas.* The Mafter-Cat came at laft to a ftately caftle, the mafter of which was an *Ogre,* the richeft that ever was known; for all the land that the King had then gone over belong'd to this caftle. The Cat, who had taken care to inform himfelf who this *Ogre* was, and what he could do, asked to fpeak with him, faving, he would not pafs fo near his caftle, without having the honour of paying his re pects to him.

THE *Ogre* received him as civilly as an *Ogre* could do, and made h m fit down. I have been affured, faid the Cat, that you have the power of changing yourfelf into all
forts

forts of creatures you have a mind
to; you can, for example, tranf-
form your felf into a lion, an ele-
phant, and the like. This is true,
faid the *Ogre* very briskly, and to
convince you, you fhall fee me now
a lion. 'The Cat was fo much
frighted to fee a lion ftand before
him, that he immediately got upon
the gutters, not without a great
deal of trouble and danger, becaufe
of his boots, which were of no
ufe to him at all in walking upon
the tiles. Some time after, when
the Cat faw that he had taken
his natural form, he came down,
and owned he had been very much
frightened. I have been moreover
informed, faid the Cat, but I.knew
not how to believe it, that you
have alfo the power to take on
you the fhape of the fmalleft animals; for example, to change your
felf into a rat or a moufe, but I
muft own to you, I take this to be
impoffible. Impoffible! faid the
Ogre,

Ogre, you fhall fee that prefently,
and at the fame time changed himfelf into a moufe that began to run
about the floor. The Cat no
fooner perceived this, but he fell
upon him, and eat him up.

THE King in the mean while,
who faw, as he paffed, this fine
caftle of the *Ogre*'s, had a mind to
come into it. The Cat, who heard
the noife of the coach running
over the draw-bridge, ran out, and
faid to the King, Your Majefty is
welcome to this caftle of my Lord
Marquifs of *Carabas.* What, my
Lord Marquifs, faid the King,
and does this caftle alfo belong to
you? there can be nothing finer than
this court, and all thefe ftately
buildings that furround it; let us
go into it, if you pleafe. The
Marquifs gave his hand to the
Princefs, and followed the King,
who went up firft; they came into
a great hall, where they found a
mag-

magnificent collation, which the *Ogre* had prepared for his friends, who were that very day to come to fee him, but dared not enter, knowing the King was there. The King was quite charmed with the good Qualities of my Lord Marquifs of *Carabas*, as was his daughter, who was fallen extremely in love with him; and feeing the vaft eftate he poffeffed, faid to him, after having drunk five or fix glaffes, it will be owing to yourfelf only, my Lord Marquifs, if you are not my fon-in-law. The Marquifs making feveral low bows, accepted the honour the King conferred upon him, and married the fame day the Princefs forthwith.

THE Cat became a great Lord, and never ran more after mice, but for his diverfion.

The

The MORAL.

HOw advantageous ere it be,
 By long deſcent of pedegree,
  T' enjoy a great eſtate.
Yet knowledge how to aᵭt we ſee,
Joyn'd with conſummate Induſtry,
  Nor wonder ye thereat,
Is for the general of it ſelf alone
To be more uſeful to young people
 known.

ANOTHER.

IF a miller's ſon gains ſo ſudden the
 heart
Of a beautiful Princeſs, and makes
 her impart
Sweet languiſhing glances, eyes dy-
 ing for love,
It muſt be remark'd of fine clothes
 how they move.

      And

*And that youth, a good face, a good
     air and good mien.
Are not always indifferent mediums
     to win
The hearts of the fair, and gently
     inspire
The flames of sweet passion, and ten-
     der desire.*

CIN-

CINDERILLA:

OR,

The little GLASS SLIPPER.

TALE VI.

 HERE was once upon a time, a gentleman who married for his fecond wife the proudeft and moft haughty woman that ever was known. She had been a widow, and had by her former

E   huſ-

husband two daughters of her own humour, who were exactly like her in all things. He had also by a former wife a young daughter, but of an unparallelled goodness and sweetness of temper, which she took from her mother, who was the best creature in the world.

No sooner were the ceremonies of the wedding over, but the mother-in-law began to display her ill humour; she could not bear the good qualities of this pretty girl; and the less, because they made her own daughters so much the more hated and despised. She employed her in the meanest work of the house, she cleaned the dishes and stands, and rubbed Madam's chamber, and those of the young Madams her daughters: she lay on the top of the house in a garret, upon a wretched straw bed, while her sisters lay in fine rooms, with floors all inlaid, upon beds of the
newest

newest fashion, and where they had
looking-glasses so large, that they
might see themselves at their full
length, from head to foot. The
poor girl bore all patiently, and
dared not tell her father, who
would have rattled her off; for his
wife governed him intirely. When
she had done her work, she used to
go into the chimney corner, and
sit down upon the cinders, which
made her commonly be called in
the house *Cinderbreech*: but the
youngest, who was not so rude and
uncivil as the eldest, called her *Cinderilla*. However, *Cinderilla*, notwithstanding her poor clothes, was
a hundred times handsomer than
her sisters, though they wore the
most magnificent apparel.

No w, it happened that the
King's son gave a ball, and invited
all persons of quality to it: our
young ladies were also invited; for
they made a very great figure.

They

They were very well pleafed thereat, and were very bufy in choofing
out fuch gowns, petticoats, and
head-clothes as might become them
beft.   This was a new trouble to
Cinderilla; for it was fhe that
ironed her fifters linnen, and plait-
ed their ruffles; they talked all day
long of· nothing but how they
fhould be drefs'd.   For my part,
faid the eldeft, I'll wear my red
velvet fuit, with French trimming.
And I, faid the youngeft, will have
my common petticoat; but then,
to make amends for that, I'll put
on my gold flowered manteau, and
my diamond ftomacher, which is
not the moft indifferent in the
world.   They fent for the beft tire-
woman they could get, to drefs their
heads, and adjuft their double pin-
ners, and they had their red brufhes
and patches from Mrs. *De la poche.*

Cinderilla advifed them the beft
in ·the world, and offered herfelf

to drefs their heads; which they
were very willing fhe fhould do.
As fhe was doing this, they faid to
her, *Cinderilla*, would you not be
glad to. go to the ball? Ah! faid
fhe, you only banter me; it is not
for fuch as I am to go thither.
You are in the right of it, faid
they, it would make the people
laugh to fee a *Cinderbreech* at a
ball. Any one but *Cinderilla* would
have dreffed their heads awry;
but fhe was very good, and drefs'd
them perfectly well. They were
almoft two days without eating, fo
much were they tranfported with
joy: they broke above a dozen of
laces in trying to be laced up clofe,
that they might have a fine flender
fhape, and they were continually
at their looking-glafs. At laft the
happy day came; they went to
court, and *Cinderilla* followed them
with her eyes as long as fhe could,
and when fhe had loft fight of
them, fhe fell a crying.

E 3   HER

HER godmother, who saw her all in tears, asked her what was the matter? I wish I could——, I wish I could——; she could not speak the rest, her tears interrupting her. Her godmother, who was a Fairy, said to her, Thou wishest thou could'st go to the ball, is it not so? Y——es, said *Cinderilla*, with a great Sob. Well, said her godmother, be but a good girl, and I'll contrive thou shalt go. Then she took her into her chamber, and said to her, go into the garden, and bring me a pompion; *Cinderilla* went immediately to gather the finest she could get, and brought it to her Godmother, not being able to imagine how this pompion could make her go to the ball: her godmother scooped out all the inside of it, having left nothing but the rind; she struck it with her wand, and the pompion immediately was turned into a fine coach, gilt all over with gold.

After

After that, she went to look into
her moufe-trap, where she found
fix mice all alive; she ordered *Cinderilla* to lift up a little the trap
door, and she gave every moufe
that went out a ftroke with her
wand, and the moufe was that moment turned into a fine horfe,
which all together made a very fine
fet of fix horfes, of a beautiful
moufe-coloured dapple grey. As she
was at a lofs for a coach-man, I'll
go and fee, fays *Cinderilla*, if there
be never a rat in the rat-trap, we'll
make a coach-man of him. You
are in the right, faid her godmother, go and fee. *Cinderilla* brought
the trap to her, and in it there
were three huge rats: the Fairy
made choice of one of the three,
which had the largeft beard, and
having touched him with her wand,
he was turned into a fat jolly coach-
man, that had the fineft whiskers·
as ever were feen.

E 4   AFTER

AFTER that, she said to her, Go into the garden, and you will find six Lizards behind the watering-pot, bring them to me; she had no sooner done so, but her godmother turned them into six footmen, who skipped up immediately behind the coach, with their liveries all be-daubed with gold and silver, and clung so close behind one another, as if they had done nothing else all their lives. The Fairy then said to *Cinderilla*, Well, you see here an equipage fit to go to the Ball with; are you not pleased with it? O yes, said she, but must I go thither as I am, with these ugly nasty clothes? Her godmother only just touched her with her wand, and at the same instant her clothes were turned into cloth of gold and silver, all beset with jewels : after this, she gave her a pair of Glass Slippers, the finest in the world. Being thus dress'd out she
got

got into her coach; but her godmother, above all things, commanded her not to ftay beyond twelve
a clock at night; telling her at the
fame time, that if fhe ftay'd at the
ball one moment longer, her coach
would be a pompion again, her
horfes mice, her footmen lizards,
and her clothes refume their old
form.

SHE promifed her godmother
fhe would not fail of leaving the
ball before midnight, and then departed not a little joyful at her
good fortune. The King's fon,
who was informed that a great
Princefs, whom they did not know,
was come, ran out to receive her;
he gave her his hand as fhe alighted
out of the coach, and led her into
the hall where the company was:
there was a great filence; they left
off dancing, and the violins ceafed
to play, fo attentive was every body
to contemplate the extraordinary
E 5 beauties

beauties of this unknown perſon:
there was heard nothing but a con-
fuſed noiſe of ha! how handſome
ſhe is, ha! how handſome ſhe is.
The King himſelf, as old as he
was, could not help looking at her,
and telling the Queen in a low
voice, that it was a long time ſince
that he had ſeen ſo beautiful and
lovely a creature. All the ladies
were buſied in conſidering her
clothes and head-dreſs, that they
might have ſome made the next
day after the ſame pattern, ſuppo-
ſing they might get ſuch fine ma-
terials, and as able hands to make
them.

THE King's ſon ſhewed her to
the moſt honourable place, and afterwards took her out to dance
with him: ſhe danced with ſo much
gracefulneſs, that they more and
more admired her. A fine collation was ſerved up, of which the
young Prince eat nothing, ſo much
4   was

was he taken up in looking upon
her. She went and ſet herſelf down
by her ſiſters, and ſhewed them a
thouſand civilities: ſhe gave them
ſome of the oranges and lemons
that the Prince had preſented.her
with; which very much ſurpriſed
them; for they did not know her.
While the company was thus employed, *Cinderilla* heard the clock
go eleven and three quarters;
upon which ſhe immediately made
a courteſy to the company, and
went away as faſt as ſhe could.

ASSOON as ſhe came home, ſhe
went to find out her godmother,
and after having thanked her, ſhe
told her, ſhe could not but heartily
wiſh to go the next day to the ball,
becauſe the King's ſon had deſired
her. As ſhe was buſie in telling
her godmother every thing that
had paſſed at the ball, her two
ſiſters knock'd at the door, *Cinderilla* went and opened it. You have
ſtay'd

ftay'd a long while, faid fhe, gap-
ing, rubbing her eyes, and ftretching herfelf as if fhe had been juft
awaked out of her fleep; fhe had
however no manner of inclination
to fleep fince they went from home.
If thou hadft been at the ball, faid
one of her fifters, thou would'ft
not have been tired with it : there
came thither the moft beautiful
Princefs, the moft beautiful that
ever was feen; fhe fhewed us a
thoufand civilities, and gave us
oranges and lemons. *Cinderilla*
feem'd indifferent; fhe asked them
the name of that Princefs; but
they told her they did not know it,
and that the King's fon was very
uneafy on her account, and would
give all the world to know where
fhe was. At this *Cinderilla* fmiled,
and faid, fhe muft then be very
handfome indeed; Lord how happy have you been, could not I fee
her? Ah! good Madam *Charlotte*,
lend me your yellow fuit of clothes
that

that you wear every day. Undoubtedly, ſaid Madam *Charlotte,*
lend my clothes to ſuch a Cinderbreech as you are, who is fool then ?
Cinderilla was very glad of the re-
fuſal, for ſhe would have been ſadly
put to it, if her ſiſter had lent her
her clothes.

THE next day the two ſiſters
were at the ball, and ſo was *Cinderilla,* but dreſſed more richly
than ſhe was at firſt. The King's
ſon was always by her, and ſaying
abundance of tender things to her;
the young lady was no ways tired,
and forgot what her godmother
had recommended to her, ſo that
ſhe heard the clock begin to ſtrike
twelve, when ſhe thought it was
only eleven, ſhe then roſe up and
fled as nimble as a deer: the
Prince followed her, but could not
catch hold of her; ſhe dropt one
of her Glaſs Slippers, which the
Prince took up very carefully; *Cin-*
derilla

derilla came home quite out of
breath, without coach or footmen,
and in her old ugly clothes; she
had nothing left her of all her
finery, but one of the little Slippers,
fellow to that she drop'd. The
guards at the palace-gate were
asked if they had not seen a Princess go out, who said, they had
seen no body go out, but a young
woman very badly dress'd, and who
had more the air of a poor country
wench than a lady.

WHEN the two sisters returned
from the ball, *Cinderilla* asked
them, if they had been well diverted, and if the fine lady had been
there; they told her, Yes, but
that she flew away assoon as it had
struck twelve a clock, and with so
much haste, that she drop'd one of
her little Glass Slippers, the prettiest
in the world, and which the King's
son had taken up, that he did nothing but look at her all the time
of

of the ball, and that certainly he
was very much in love with the
beautiful perſon who owned the
little Slipper. What they ſaid was
very true; for a few days after,
the King's ſon cauſed it to be pro-
claimed by ſound of trumpet, that
he would marry her whoſe foot
this Slipper would juſt fit. They
began to try it on upon the prin-
ceſſes, then the dutcheſſes, and all
the court, but in vain; it was
brought to the two ſiſters, who
did all they poſſibly could to thruſt
their foot into the Slipper, but they
could not effect it. *Cinderilla*, who
ſaw all this, and knew the Slipper,
ſaid to them laughing, Let me ſee
if it will not fit me; her ſiſters
burſt out a laughing, and began to
banter her. The gentleman who
was ſent to try the Slipper, looked
earneſtly at *Cinderilla*, and finding
her very handſome, ſaid, it was
but juſt that ſhe ſhould try, and
that he had orders to let every body

dy do fo. He made *Cinderilla* fit down, and putting the Slipper to her foot, he found it went in very eafily, and fitted her, as if it had been made of wax. The aftonifh-ment her two fifters were in, were very great; but much greater, when *Cinderilla* pulled out of her pocket the other Slipper, and put it upon her foot. Upon this her godmother came in, who having touch'd with her wand *Cinderilla*'s clothes, made them more rich and magnificent than ever they were before.

AND now, her two fifters found her to be that fine beautiful lady that they had feen at the ball. They threw themfelves at her feet, to beg pardon for all the ill treat-ment they had made her undergo. *Cinderilla* took them up, and told them, as fhe embraced them, that fhe forgave them with all her heart, and defired them always to love her.

her. She was conducted to the
young Prince dreſs'd as ſhe was: he
thought her more beautiful than
ever, and a few days after married
her. *Cinderilla,* who was as good
as handſome, gave her two ſiſters
lodgings in the palace, and married them the ſame day to two great
lords of the court.

The MORAL.

BEauty's *to the ſex a treaſure,*
  We ſtill admire it without mea-
      ſure,
And never yet was any known
By ſtill admiring weary grown.
But that thing, which we call good
    grace,
Exceeds by far a handſome face ;
Its charms by far ſurpaſs the other,
And this was what her good god-
    mother
Beſtow'd on CINDERILLA *fair,*
Whom ſhe inſtructed with ſuch care,
                              And

And gave her such a graceful mien,
That she became thereby a Queen.
For thus (may ever truth prevail)
We draw our moral from this Tale.
This quality, fair ladies, know
Prevails much more, you'll find it so,
T'engage and captivate a heart,
Than a fine head dress'd up with art;
'Tis the true gift of heaven and fate,
Without it none in any state
Effectual any thing can do;
But with it all things well and true.

ANOTHER.

A Great advantage 'tis, no doubt,
        to man,
To have wit, courage, birth, good
        sense and brain,
And other such like Qualities, which
        we
Receiv'd from heaven's kind hand and
        destiny.

But

But none of theſe rich graces from
    above,
In your advancement in the world
    will prove
Of any uſe, if Godſires make delay,
Or Godmothers your merit to diſplay.

RIQUET

RIQUET

A la HOUPE.

TALE VII.

 HERE was once upon
a time a Queen, who
was brought to bed of a
ſon, ſo deform'd, and ſo
very ugly, that they were
a long while doubting, whether he
had human ſhape. A Fairy, who
was

was at his birth, faid, he would
be very aimable for all that, for he
would have a great deal of wit;
fhe added moreover, that it fhould
be in his power, by virtue of a
gift fhe had given him, to give as
much wit as he pleafed to the perfon he fhould love beft. All this
fomewhat comforted the poor
Queen, who was under a very great
affliction, for having brought into
the world fuch an ugly Marmot.
It is true, that this child no fooner
began to prattle, but he faid a
thoufand pretty things, and had
fomething of I know not what of
fuch a wittinefs, that he charmed
every body. I forgot to tell you,
that he came into the world with a
little *Houpe* *, or Tuft of hair
upon his head, which made them
call him *Riquet a la Houpe*; for
Riquet was the name of the family.

* *Houpe* fignifies a Tuft.

SEVEN

SEVEN or eight years after this,
the Queen of a neighbouring kingdom was brought to bed of two
daughters, the firſt that came into
the world was fairer than the day:
the Queen was ſo very glad at it,
that they were afraid that her exceſs of joy would do her harm.
The ſame Fairy, who had aſſiſted
at the birth of little *Riquet a la*
Houpe, was preſent; and to moderate the joy of the Queen, ſhe declared that this little Princeſs
ſhould have no manner of wit, but
ſhould be as ſtupid as ſhe was
handſome. This very much mor-
tified the Queen; but ſome moments afterwards ſhe had far greater ſorrow; for the ſecond daughter ſhe was delivered of, was extremely ugly. Do not afflict your
ſelf ſo much, Madam, ſaid the
Fairy: your daughter ſhall have it
made up to her otherwiſe, and ſhe
ſhall have ſo great a ſhare of wit,
that

that scarce any body shall perceive
her want of beauty. God grant it,
said the Queen; but is there no
way to make the eldest, who is so
very handsome, have any wit? I
can do nothing for her, Madam,
as to wit, replied the Fairy, but
every thing as to beauty: and as
there is nothing but what I would
do for your satisfaction, *I give her
for gift,* that she shall have the
power to make handsome the person who shall best please her.

In proportion, as these Princesses
grew up, their perfections grew up
with them; all the publick talk
was of the beauty of the eldest,
and the wit of the youngest. It
is true also, that their defects
greatly increased with their age;
the youngest had an ugly turn of
her eyes, and the eldest grew every
day more and more stupid; she either made no answer at all to what
was asked her, or said somewhat
very

very filly; fhe was with all this fo
very unhandy, that fhe could not
place four pieces of *China* upon the
mantle-piece, without breaking one
of them, nor drink a glafs of water without fpilling half of it upon
her clothes. Though beauty is a
very great advantage in young people, yet here the youngeft fifter
carried away the bell almoft always
in all companies from the eldeft;
they would go up indeed to the
Beauty to look upon and admire
her, but turn afide foon after to
the *Wit*, to hear a thoufand things
the moft entertaining and agreeable;
and it was amazing to fee in lefs
than a quarter of an hour's time,
the eldeft with not a foul with her,
and the whole company crowd'ng
about the youngeft. The eldeft,
though fhe was very ftupid, took
particular notice of it, and would
have given all her beauty to have
half the wit of her fifter. The
Queen, as fage as fhe was, could
not

not help reproaching her feveral times, which had like to have made this poor Princefs die for grief.

ONE day, as fhe retired into the wood to bewail her misfortune, fhe faw running up to her, a little man very difagreeable, but moft magnificently and richly drefs'd. This was the young Prince *Riquet a la Houpe*, who having fallen in love with her, by feeing her picture, which went all the world over, had left his father's kingdom, to have the pleafure of feeing and talking with her ; overjoy'd to find her thus all alone, he addreffed himfelf to her with all the civility and refpect imaginable. Having obferved, after he had made his ordinary complements, that fhe was extremely melancholy, he faid to her, I cannot comprehend, Madam, how a perfon fo beautiful as you are, can be fo forrowful as you feem to be ;

F   for

for though I can boaſt of having
ſeen an infinite number of ladies
exquiſitely handſome, I cannot ſay
that ever I ſaw any one whoſe beauty comes near yours. You are
pleaſed to ſay ſo, ſaid the Princeſs;
and here ſhe ſtopp'd. Beauty, replied *Riquet a la Houpe,* is ſo great
an advantage, that it ought to take
place of every thing; and ſince you
poſſeſs this Treaſure, I ſee nothing
can poſſibly very much afflict or
trouble you. I had much rather,
ſaid the Princeſs, be as ugly as
you are, and have wit, than have
the beauty I poſſeſs, and be ſo ſtupid as I am. There is nothing,
Madam, replied he, ſhews more
that we have wit, than to believe
we have none; and it is the nature
of that excellent quality, that the
more people have of it, the more
they believe they want it. I do
not know that, ſaid the Princeſs,
but I know very well, that I am
very dull and ſtupid, and hence
pro-

proceeds the exceſſive *Chagrin* and uneaſineſs that almoſt kills me.

If that be all, Madam, which troubles you, I can very eaſily put an end to your affliction. And how? ſaid the Princeſs. I have the power, Madam, ſaid *Riquet a la Houpe*, to give to that perſon whom I muſt love beſt, as much of that excellent quality as poſſibly can be made uſe of; and as you, Madam, are that very perſon, it will be your fault only, if you have not as great a ſhare of it as any one living, provided you will reſolve ſeriouſly to marry me. The Princeſs was ſtruck quite dumb at theſe words, ſhe could not anſwer a ſyllable. I ſee, replied *Riquet a la Houpe*, that this propoſal makes you very uneaſy, and I do not wonder at it; but I will give you a whole year to conſider of it.

F 2 THE

THE Princess had so little wit, and so great a desire of having some, that she imagined the end of that year would never be; so that she accepted of the proposal that was made to her. She had no sooner promised *Riquet a la Houpe*, that she would marry him on that day twelve-month, than she found herself quite otherwise than she was before; she had an incredible facility of speaking whatever she had a mind, and that too, after a fine, easy and natural manner: she began that moment a very agreeable conversation with *Riquet a la Houpe*, where she tattled so powerfully that *Riquet a la Houpe* believed he had given her more wit than he had reserved for himself.

WHEN she returned to the palace, the whole court knew not what to think of such a sudden and

2

and extraordinary change ; for they
heard from her now as much fenfible
difcourfe, and as many infinitely
witty turns, as they had ftupid and
filly impertinencies before. The
whole court was fo much overjoyed at it, as was beyond imagination ; every body was well
pleafed, but her fifter ; becaufe
having no longer the advantage of
her in refpect of wit, fhe appeared in comparifon of her a very
difagreeable old Pufs. The King
governed himfelf by her advice,
and would even fometimes hold a
council in her apartment. The
noife of this change fpreading itfelf
every where, all the young princes
of the neighbouring kingdoms
ftrove all they could to get into her
good graces; and almoft all of
them asked her in marriage ; but
fhe found not one of them had wit
enough for her, and fhe heard
their courtfhip, but would engage
herfelf to none of them. How-

F 3   ever,

ever, there came one so powerful,
rich, witty and handsome, that she
could not help having a good Inclination for him. Her father perceived it, and told her, that she
was her own mistress as to the
choice of a husband, and that she
might declare her intentions. As
the more wit we have, the greater
difficulty we find to make a firm
resolution upon such an affair; this
made her desire her Father, after
having thanked him, to give her
time to consider of it. She went
accidentally to walk in the same
wood where she met *Riquet a la
Houpe*, to think the more conveni-
ently what she had to do. While
she was walking in a profound medi-
tation, she heard a confused noise
under her feet, as it were of a great
many people that went backwards
and forwards, and were very busy.
Having listened more attentively, she
heard one say, bring me that pot;
another, give me that kettle; and a
third,

third, put fome wood upon the
fire. The ground at the fame time
opened, and fhe faw under her feet,
as it were, a great kitchen full of
cooks, fcullions, and all forts of
officers neceffary for a magnificent
entertainment. There came out of
it a company of roafters, to the
number of twenty, or thirty, who
went to plant themfelves in an
alley of the wood about a very
long table, with their larding pins
in their hands, and foxes-tails in
their caps, who began to work in
time, to the tune of a very har-
monious fong. The Princefs, all
aftonifhed at this fight, asked
them whom they worked for? For
Prince *Riquet a la Houpe*, faid the
foremoft of them, who is to be
married to morrow. The Princefs
more fuprifed than ever, and re-
collecting that it was now that day
twelvemonth that fhe had promifed
to marry *Riquet a la Houpe*, fhe was
like to fink to the ground: what

F 4   made

made her forget this, was, that
when she made this promise, she
was very silly, and having gotten a
vast stock of wit which the Prince
had bestowed on her, she had entirely forgotten her stupidity. She
continued walking, but had not
taken thirty steps before *Riquet
a la Houpe* presented himself to her,
bravely and most magnificently
dress'd, like a prince who was going
to be married. You see, Madam,
said he, I am very exact in keeping my word, and doubt not in the
least but you are come hither to
keep yours, and to make me, by
giving me your hand, the happiest
of men. I shall freely own to you,
answered the Princess, that I have
not yet taken any resolution on
this affair, and believe I never shall
take such a one as you desire. You
astonish me, Madam, said *Riquet
a la Houpe.* I believe it, said the
Princess, and surely if I had to do
with a clown, or a man of no wit,
                                I should

I should find my self very much at a loss. A princess is as good as her word, would he say to me, and you must marry me, since you promised to do so. But as he whom I talk to is the man of the world who is master of the greatest sense and judgment, I am sure he will hear reason. You know, that when I was but very silly, I could notwithstanding never come to a Resolution to marry you, why will you have me, now I have so much judgment as you gave me, and which makes me a more difficult person than I was at that time, to come to such a Resolution, which I could not then determine to agree to? If you sincerely thought to make me your wife, you have been much in the wrong to deprive me of my dull simplicity, and make me see things much more clearly than I did.

F 5   It

IF a man of no wit and fenfe, replied *Riquet a la Houpe*, would be well received, as you fay, in reproaching you for breach of your word, why will you not let me, Madam, have the fame ufage in an affair, where all the happinefs of my life is concern'd? is it reafonable that perfons of wit and fenfe fhould be in a worfe condition than thofe who have none? can you pretend this, you who have fo great a fhare, and defired fo earneftly to have it? But let us come to fact, if you pleafe. Setting afide my uglinefs and deformity, is there any thing in me that difpleafes you? are you diffatisfy'd with my birth? my wit, humour or manners? Not at all, anfwered the Princefs, I love and refpect in you all what you mention. If it be fo, faid *Riquet a la Houpe*, I am happy; fince it is in your power to make me the moft aimable of men. How

can

can that be, faid the Princefs? It
is done, faid *Riquet a la Houpe,* if
you love me enough to wifh it
were fo; and that you may no-
ways doubt, Madam, of what I
fay, know that the fame Fairy who
on my birth day, *gave me for Gift*
the power of making the perfon,
who fhould pleafe me, extremely
witty and judicious, has in like
manner *given you for gift* the power of making him whom you love,
and would grant that favour to, be
extremely handfome. If it be fo,
faid the Princefs, I wifh with all
my heart, that you may be the
moft aimable prince in the world,
and I will give you this rare gift,
as much as is in my power.

THE Princefs had no fooner pro-
nounced thefe words, but *Riquet
a la Houpe* appeared to her the
fineft Prince in the world, the moft
handfome and moft aimable that e-
ver was known. Some authors affirm,
that

that this was not owing to the charms of the Fairy, which worked this change, but love alone caufed the Metamorphofis. They fay, that the Princefs having made due reflection on the perfeverance of her lover, his difcretion, and all the good qualities of his mind, his wit and judgment, faw no longer the deformity of his body, nor the ugdinefs of his face; that his hump feem'd to her no more than the air of one who had a broad back; and that whereas till then fhe faw him frightfully lame, fhe found it nothing more than a certain bending air, which charm'd her. They fay further, that his eyes, which were very fquinting, feem'd to her moft bright and fparkling, that their irregular turns pafs'd in her judgment for a mark of a violent excefs of love; and, in fhort, that his great red nofe had, in her opinion, fomewhat of the martial and heroick. However it was, the
Prin-

Princess promised immediately to
marry him, on condition he ob-
tain'd her father's consent.   The
King being acquainted, that his
daughter had a great deal of esteem
for *Riquet a la Houpe*, whom he
knew otherwise for a most sage and
judicious prince, received him for
his son-in-law with pleasure; and
the next morning their nuptials
were celebrated, as *Riquet a la
Houpe* had foreseen, and according
to the orders he had a long time
before given.

The MORAL.

WHat in this little tale we find
*   Is less a fable than the real*
*   truth.*
In whom we love appear rare gifts
*   of mind*
And body too : wit, judgment, beauty,
*   youth.*

'ANO-

ANOTHER.

AN objeɛt, *where are drawn by na-*
     ture's hand,
Beautiful traces, and the lively ſtain
Of ſuch complexion art can ne'er
     attain,
With all their gifts have not ſo much
     command
On hearts, as hath one ſecret charm
     alone
Love there finds out, to all beſides
     unknown.

Little

LITTLE POUCET,
AND
His two BROTHERS.

TALE VIII

HERE was once upon a time a man and his wife, who made faggots for their livelihood, they had seven children all boys. The eldest was but ten years old, and the youngest but seven.

feven. People were amazed, that the faggot-maker had fo many children in fo fmall a time; but it was becaufe his wife went quick about her bufinefs, and brought never lefs than two at a time. They were very poor, and their feven children incommoded them very much; becaufe not one of them was able to get his bread. That which gave them yet more uneafinefs, was, that the youngeft was of a very tender conftitution, and fcarce ever fpoke a word, which made them take that for ftupidity, which was a fign of good fenfe; he was very little, and was no bigger when he was born than one's thumb, which made him be called *Little Poucet,* which fignifies little Thumb.

THE poor child bore the blame of every thing that was done amifs in the houfe, and he was always in the wrong: he was, notwithftanding

ſtanding all this, more cunning,
and had a far greater ſhare of wiſdom than all his brothers put together; and if he ſpoke little, he
heard and thought the more.

THERE happen'd now to come
a very bad year, and the famine
was ſo great, that theſe poor people reſolved to rid themſelves of
their children. One evening, when
they were all in bed, and the faggot-
maker was ſitting with his wife at the
fire, he ſaid to her, with his heart
ready to break with grief, Thou
ſeeſt, *Mary*, that we cannot keep
our children, and I cannot ſee them
die before my face; I am reſolved
to loſe them in the wood to-morrow, which may very eaſily be
done; for while they are buſy in
tying up the faggots, we may run
away, and leave them, without their
taking the leaſt notice. Ah! cried
out his wife, and canſt thou thy
ſelf, *Nicholas*, have the heart to
take

take the children out along with thee, on purpose to lose them? In vain did her husband reprefent to her their extreme poverty, fhe would not confent to it; fhe was poor it was true, but fhe was their mother. However, having confidered what a grief it would be to her to fee them die with hunger, fhe at laft confented, and went to bed all in tears.

Little Poucet heard every thing that was faid; for having underftood, as he lay in his bed, by fome certain words, what they were talking of, he got up very foftly, and flid himfelf under his father's ftool, that he might hear what they faid, without being feen himfelf. He went to bed again, but did not fleep a wink all the reft of the night, thinking on what he had to do. He got up early in the morning, and went to the river's fide, where he filled his
pockets

pockets full of small white pebbles,
and then returned home. They
all went abroad, but *Little Poucet*
never told his brothers one syllable
of what he knew. They went into a very thick forrest, where they
could not see one another at ten
feet distance. The Faggot-maker
began to cut wood, and the children to gather up the branches to
make faggots. Their father and
mother seeing them busy at their
work, got from them insensibly,
and then ran away from them all
at once, through the winding
bushes. When the children saw
they were left alone, they began
to cry as loud as they could.
Little Poucet let them cry on,
knowing very well how to get
home again; for as he came
out, he dropt all along the way
the little white pebbles he had
in his pockets. Then he said to
them, don't be afraid, Brothers,
Father and Mother have left us
here

here, but I'll bring you home again,
only follow me; they did so, and
he brought them home by the very
same way that they came into the
forrest: they dared not go in, but
sat themselves down at the door,
to hear what their Father and
Mother said.

THE very moment that the Faggot-maker and his Wife came home,
the lord of the manour sent them
ten crowns which he had owed
them a long while, and which
they never expected to see, This
gave them new life; for the poor
people were dying for hunger.
The Faggot-maker sent his Wife
immediately to the butchers, As it
was a long while since they had
eaten any thing, they bought three
times as much meat as would sup
two people: when they had eaten
their fill, his wife said, Alas!
where are now our poor children?
they would make a good feast of
what

what we have left; but as it was
you, *Nicholas*, who had a mind to
lofe them, I told you we fhould
repent of it, what are they now
doing in the forreft? Alas! dear
God, the wolves have eaten them
up: thou haft been very inhumane
thus to have loft thy children.

THE Faggot-maker grew at laft
extremely angry, for fhe repeated
it above twenty times, that they
fhould repent of it, and that fhe
was in the right of it for fo fay-
ing. He threatened to beat her, if
fhe did not hold her tongue. It was
not that the Faggot-maker was not
perhaps more forry than his Wife,
but that fhe continually teized him,
and that he was of the humour of
a great many others, who love thofe
wives who fpeak well, but think
thofe very importunate that have
always done fo. She was all in tears:
Alas! where are now my children,
my poor children? She fpoke this
once

once, so very loud, that the children who were at the door, began to cry out altogether, Here we are, here we are: she ran immediately to open the door, and said to them as she kissed them, I am glad to see you, my dear children, you are very hungry and weary; and *Billy*, you are very dirty, come in and let me clean you. Now, you must know, that *Billy* was her eldest son, which she loved above all the rest, because he was somewhat red-hair'd, as she herself was. They sat down to supper, and eat with such an appetite as pleased both father and mother, to whom they told how much afraid they were in the forrest, speaking almost always all together. This good couple were extremely glad to see their children once more at home; and this joy continued as long as the ten crowns lasted; but when the money was all gone, they fell again into their former uneasiness, and re-

solved

folved to lofe them once more;
and that they might be the more
certain of it, to carry them at a
much greater diftance than they
had done before. They could not
talk of this fo fecretly, but *Little
Poucet* heard it, who made account
to get out of this difficulty as well
as the former; but though he got
up very betimes in the morning, to
go and pick up fome little pebbles,
he was difappointed; for the door
of the houfe was double-locked.
He was at a ftand what to do;
when their Father had given each
of them a piece of bread for their
breakfaft, he fancied he might make
ufe of his piece in ftead of the
pebbles, by throwing it in little bits
all along the way they fhould pafs;
he put it up therefore very clofe
into his pocket. Their Father and
Mother brought them into the
thickeft and moft obfcure part of
the forreft, and when they were
there, they got to a by-path, and
left

left them there. *Little Poucet* was not uneafy at it; for he thought he could very eafily find the way again, by means of his bread which he had fcattered all the way he went; but he was very much furprized, when he could not find fo much as one crumb; the birds came and had eaten it up every bit. They were now in a great deal of trouble; for they wandered ftill more and more out of their way, and were more and more bewildered in the forreft.

NIGHT now came on, and there arofe a very great wind, which made them dreadfully afraid; they fancied they heard on every fide of them the howling of wolves that were coming to eat them up; they fcarce dared to fpeak or turn their heads. After this, it rained very hard, which wetted them to the skin; their feet flipped at every ftep they took, and they fell into the mire, whence

whence they got up in a very dirty condition, and were forced to go upon all four. *Little Poucet* climbed up to the top of a tree, to see if he could discover any thing; having turned his head about on every side, he saw at last a glimmering light, as it were of a candle, but a long way from the forrest: he came down, and then he could see nothing of it; which made him very comfortless. However, having walked for some time with his brothers towards that side on which he had seen the light; he perceived it again when they came out of the wood.

THEY came at last to a house where this candle was, not without abundance of fear; for very often they lost fight of it, which happened every time they came into a bottom. They knocked at the door, and a good woman came and opened it; she asked them what
G   they

they would have ; *Little Poucet* told
her, they were poor children, that
had been loft in the forreft, and defired to lodge there for God's fake.
The woman feeing them fo very
pretty, began to weep, and faid to
them, Alas! poor children, whence
came ye; ' do you know that this
houfe belongs to an *Ogre*, that eats
up little children? Ah! dear Madam, anfwered *Little Poucet*, who
trembled every joint of him, as
well as his brothers, what fhall we
do? it is moft certain, that the
wolves of the forreft will not fail
to eat us to night, if you refufe
us to lie here; and this being fo,
we would rather the gentleman
your husband fhould eat us, and
perhaps he may take pity upon us,
efpecially if you intercede with
him. The *Ogre's* wife, who believed fhe could conceal them from
her husband till the morning, let
them come in, and brought them
into the kitchen, that they might

warm

warm themfelves at a very good
fire; for there was a whole fheep
upon the fpit roafting for the *Ogre*'s
fupper. As they began to warm
themfelves, they heard three or
four great raps at the door; this
was the *Ogre* that was come home.
Upon this fhe hid them under the
bed, and went to open the door.
The *Ogre* then asked if fupper was
ready, and the wine drawn, and
then fat himfelf down to table.
The fheep was as yet all raw and
bloody; but he liked it the better
for that. He fniffed upon the
right hand and upon the left, fay-
ing, he fmelt frefh meat; what you
fmell fo, faid his wife, muft be
the calf which I have juft now
killed and flead. I fmell frefh
meat, I tell thee once more, replied the *Ogre*, looking crofsly at
his wife, and there is fomething
here that I don't underftand; as he
fpoke thefe words, he got up from
the table, and went directly to the

G 2   **Bed.**

bed. Ah, ha! faid he, I fee then how thou would'ft cheat me, thou curfed woman, I don't know why I don't eat up thee too, but thou art an old beaft. Here is good game that comes very luckily to entertain three *Ogres* of my acquaintance, who are to come to fee me in a day or two. The poor children fell upon their knees, and begged his pardon, but they had to do with one of the moft cruel *Ogres* in the world, who, far from having any pity on them, had already devoured them with his eyes, and told his wife, they would be delicate eating, when toffed up with an anchovie, and caper fauce. He then took a great knife, and coming up to thefe poor children, whetted it upon a great whet-ftone that he had in his left hand. He had already taken hold of one of them, when his wife faid to him, what need you do it now? is it not time enough to morrow? Hold
your

your prating, faid the *Ogre*, they will eat the tenderer. But you have fo much victuals already, replied his wife, you have no occasion; here is a calf, two sheep, and half a hog. That is true, faid the *Ogre*, give them their belly full, that they may not fall away, and put them to bed.

The good woman was overjoy'd at this, and gave them a good supper, but they were fo much afraid, they could not eat a bit. As for the *Ogre*, he fat down again to drink, being highly pleafed that he had gotten wherewithal to treat his friends. He drank a dozen glaffes more than ordinary, which got up into his head, and obliged him to go to bed.

The *Ogre* had feven daughters, all little children, and thefe little *Ogreffes* had all of them very fine complexions, becaufe they

G 3 ufed

uſed to eat freſh meat like their father; but they had little grey eyes
and intirely round, hooked noſes,
very large mouths, and very long
ſharp teeth, ſtanding at a pretty
diſtance from each other. They
were not yet very wicked, but they
promiſed it very much, ſor they
had already bitten ſeveral little
children, that they might ſuck
their blood. They were put to bed
very early, and they lay all ſeven
in a great bed, with every one a
crown of gold upon her head.
There was in the ſame chamber
another bed of the ſame bigneſs,
and it was into this bed the *Ogre*'s
wiſe put the ſeven little boys, after
which ſhe went to bed to her huſ-
band. *Little Poucet,* who had ob-
ſerved that the *Ogre*'s Daughters
had crowns of gold upon their
heads, and was afraid left the *Ogre*
ſhould repent his not killing of
them, got up about midnight; and
taking his brothers bonnets and his
own

own, went very foftly, and put them
upon the heads of the feven little
Ogreſſes, after having taken off
their crowns of gold, which he
put upon his own head and his brothers, that the *Ogre* might take
them for his daughters, and his
daughters for the little boys that he
had a mind to kill. All this fuc-
ceeded according to his defire; for
the *Ogre* waking a little after, and
forry he deferred to do that till the
morning, which he might have
done over night, he threw himfelf
haftily out of bed, and taking his
great knife, Let us fee, faid he,
how our little rogues do, and not
make two jobs of the matter. He
then went up, groping all the way
into his daughters chamber; and
coming up to the bed where the
little boys lay, and who were every
foul of them faft afleep, except
Little Poucet, who was terribly
afraid when he found the *Ogre*
feeling about his head, as he had

G 4 done

done about his brothers. The *Ogre*,
who felt the crowns of gold, said,
I should have made a fine piece of
work of it truly, I find I have taken too much of the bottle laſt
night, that is certain. Then he
went to the bed where the girls
lay; and having felt the boys little
Bonnets. Hah! said he, my merry
little lads, are you there? let us
work hard; and ſaying theſe
words, he cut, without more ado,
the throats of all his ſeven little
daughters. Well pleaſed with what
he had done, he went to bed again
to his wife. Aſſoon as *Little Poucet*
heard the *Ogre* ſnore, he waked
his brothers, and bad them put on
their clothes preſently and follow
him: they ſtole down ſoftly into
the garden, and got over the wall.
They kept running almoſt all night,
and continually trembled, without
knowing which way they went.

THE

THE *Ogre,* when he awoke, faid to his wife, Go up ftairs, and drefs the little rogues that came here laft night: the *Ogrefs* was very much furprized at this goodnefs of her husband, not dreaming after what manner he intended fhe fhould drefs them ; but thinking that he had ordered her to go and put on their clothes, went up, and was very much furprized, when fhe perceived her feven daughters killed, and weltering in their own blood. She fainted away; for this is the firft expedient almoft all women find in the like misfortunes. The *Ogre* fearing his wife would be too long in doing what he had commanded her, went up himfelf to help her. He was no lefs aftonifhed than his wife, at this frightful fpectacle. Ah! what have I done? cried he, the curfed rogues fhall pay for it, and that prefently too. He threw then a pitcher of water upon his

G 5　　　　wife's

wife's face; and having brough
her to herself, give me quickly
faid he, my boots of feven leagues,
that I may go and catch them. He
went out into the high way; and
having run over a great deal of
ground both on this fide and that;
he came at laft into the very road
where the poor children were,
who were not above an hundred
paces from their father's houfe.
They fpied the *Ogre*, who went at
one ftep from mountain to mountain, and over rivers as eafily as the
narroweft gutters. *Little Poucet*
feeing a hollow rock near the place
where they were, made his brothers hide themfelves in it, and
crept into it himfelf, minding always what would become of the
Ogre.

THE *Ogre*, who found himfelf
very weary, after fo long a journey, to no manner of purpofe (for
thefe fame boots of feven leagues,
fa-

fatigue their man very much) had
a great mind to reft himfelf, and
by chance went to fit down upon
the rock where thefe little boys
had hidden themfelves. As it was
impoffible he could be more weary
than he was, he fell afleep; and
after repofing himfelf fome time,
began to fnore fo frightfully, that
the poor children were no lefs
afraid of him, than when he held
up his great knife, and was going to
cut their throats. *Little Poucet* was
not fo much frightened as his brothers, and told them, that they
fhould run away immediately towards home, while the *Ogre* flept
fo foundly, and that they fhould
not be in any pain about him.
They took his advice, and got
home prefently. *Little Poucet* came
up to the *Ogre*, pulled off his boots,
and put them on upon his own
legs; the boots were very long and
large; but as they were Fairies,
they were capable of growing big
and

and little, according to the legs of
thofe that wore them ; fo that they
fittted his feet and legs as well as if
they had been made on purpofe for
him. He went immediately to the
Ogre's houfe, where he faw his wife
crying bitterly for the lofs of her
children that were murdered.

YOUR husband, faid *Little
Poucet*, is in very great danger, being taken by a gang of thieves,
who have fworn to kill him, if he
does not give them all his gold
and filver. The very moment they
held their daggers at his throat,
he perceived me, and defired me
to come and tell you the condition
he is in, and that you fhould give
me every thing he has that is valuable, without exception; for
otherwife they will kill him without mercy: and as his cafe is very
preffing, he defires me to make
ufe (you fee I have them on) of
his boots of feven leagues, that I
might

might make the more hafte, and
to fhew you that I do not impofe
upon you.

THE good woman being very
much affrighted, gave him all fhe
had: for this *Ogre* was a very good
husband, though he ufed to eat up
little children. *Little Poucet* having thus gotten all the *Ogre*'s money, came home to his father's
houfe, where he was received with
a great deal of Joy.

THERE are a great many Authors, who do not agree in this
laft circumftance, and pretend, that
Little Poucet never robbed the
Ogre of his cafh, and that he only
thought he might very equitably,
and according to good confcience,
take off his boots of feven leagues,
becaufe he made ufe of them for
no other end, but to run after little
children. Thefe Gentlemen fay,
that they are very well affured of
this

this, and the more, as having drank
and eaten often at the Faggot-
maker's house. They say further,
that when *Little Poucet* had taken
off the *Ogre*'s boots, he went to
Court, where he was informed that
they were very much in pain about
an army that was two hundred
leagues off, and the Success of a
battle. He went, say they, to the
King, and told him, that if he defired it, he would bring him News
from the army before night. The
King promised him a great sum of
money upon that condition. *Little
Poucet* was as good as his word,
and returned that same very night
with the news; and this first expedition causing him to be known, he
got whatever he pleas'd; for the
King paid him very well for carry-
ing his orders to the army, and
abundance of ladies gave him what
he would to bring them news from
their lovers; and that this was his
greatest gain. There were some
mar-

married women too, who sent Letters by him to their husbands, but
they paid him so ill, that it was
not worth his while, and turned
to no manner of account. After
having for some time carried on
the business of a messenger, and
gained thereby a great deal of
money, he went home to his father, where it was impossible to
express the joy they were all in at
his return. He made the whole
family very easy, bought places for
his father and brothers; and by
that means settled them very hand-
somely in the world, and in the
mean time made his own court to
perfection.

The MORAL.

AT many children parents don't re-
pine,
If handsome, and their wits and
judgments shine,

Polite

Polite in carriage, and in body strong,
Graceful in mien, and elegant in
tongue.
But if one of them prove perchance
but weak,
Him they despise, laugh at, defraud
and cheat.
Such is the wretched world's curs'd
way; and yet
Sometimes this little despicable thing,
This poor Marmot, which so despised
we see,
By unforeseen Events shall honour
bring,
And happy weal to all the family.

MOTHER GOOSE'S

MELODY

Text of the Mother Goose's Melody

O My kitten a kitten,
    And oh! my kitten, my deary,
Such a sweet pap as this
There is not far nor neary;
There we go up, up, up,
Here we go down, down, down,
Here we go backwards and forwards,
And here we go round, round, round.

Maxim.

Idleness hath no advocate, but many friends.

D 3   THIS

FOREWORD

Like the *Mother Goose's Tales*, this copy of the *Mother Goose's Melody* is unique. We are grateful to Miss Elisabeth Ball, of Muncie, Indiana, for sending us the clear photographs of her treasured book which were used for reproducing the text. While our reproduction is larger than the original, the page opposite is reproduced in actual size. We do not know the identity of the illustrator, as the engravings are unsigned, but the suggestion that they are by John Bewick, the brother of Thomas, has not improbably been made recently by M. J. P. Weedon (see Bibliography).

MOTHER GOOSE's
MELODY:

OR,

Sonnets for the Cradle.

IN TWO PARTS.

PART I. Contains the most celebrated Songs and Lullabies of the old British Nurses, calculated to amuse Children and to excite them to Sleep.

PART II. Those of that sweet Songster and Nurse of Wit and Humour, Master William Shakespeare.

EMBELLISHED WITH CUTS.

And Illustrated with Notes and Maxims, Historical, Philosophical and Critical.

L O N D O N:

Printed for FRANCIS POWER, (Grandson to the late Mr. J. NEWBERY,) and Co. No. 65. St. Paul's Church-Yard, 1791.

[Price Three Pence.]

PREFACE.

By a very GREAT WRITER of very LITTLE BOOKS.

MUCH might be faid in favour of this collection, but as we have no room for critical difquifitions we fhall only obferve to our readers, that the cuftom of finging thefe fongs and lullabies to children is of great antiquity: It is even as old as the time of the ancient *Druids*. *Caractacus*, King of the *Britons*, was rocked in his cradle in the ifle of *Mona*, now called *Anglefea*, and tuned to fleep by fome of thefe foporiferous fonnets. As the beft things, however, may be made an ill ufe of, fo this kind of compofition has been employed in a fatirical manner; of which we have a remarkable inftance fo far back as the reign of king *Henry* the fifth. When that great prince turned his arms againſt *France*, he compoſed the following march to lead his troops to battle, well knowing that muſick had often the power of inſpiring courage, eſpecially in the minds of good men.

Of this his enemies took advantage,

and, as our happy nation, even at that time, was-never without a faction, some of the malecontents adopted the following words to the king's own march, in order to ridicule his majesty, and to shew the folly and impossibility of his undertaking.

There was an old woman toss'd in a
      blanket,
Seventeen times as high as the moon;
But where she was going no mortal
      could tell,
For under her arm she carried a broom:
Old woman, old woman, old woman, said I?
      man, said I?
Whither, ah whither, ah whither
      so high?
To sweep the cobwebs from the sky,
And I'll be with you by and by.

Here the king is represented as an old woman, engaged in a pursuit the most absurd and extravagant imaginable;

able; but when he had routed the whole *French* army at the battle of *Agincourt*, taking their king and the flower of their nobility prisoners, and with ten thousand men only made himself master of their kingdom; the very men who had ridiculed him before began to think nothing was too arduous for him to surmount, they therefore cancelled the former sonnet, which they were now ashamed of, and substituted this in its stead, which you will please to observe goes to the same tune.

So vast is the prowess of *Harry* the
   Great,
He'll pluck a hair from the pale-fac'd
   moon;
Or a lion familiarly take by the tooth,
And lead him about as you lead a
   baboon.

       All

All princes and potentates under the
    fun,
Through fear into corners and holes
    away run;
While nor dangers nor dread his fwift
    progrefs retards,
For he deals about kingdoms as we
    do our cards.

When this was fhewn to his majefty he fmilingly faid, that folly always
dealt in extravagancies, and that
knaves fometimes put on the garb of
fools to promote in that difguife their
own wicked defigns. " The flattery
" in the laft (fays he) is more in-
" fulting than the impudence of the
" firft, and to weak minds might do
" more mifchief; but we have the
" old proverb in our favour: *If we
" do not flatter ourfelves, the flattery of
" others will never hurt us.*"

We

We cannot conclude without ob-
ferving, the great probability there
is that the cuftom of making *Nonfenfe
Verfes* in our fchools was borrowed
from this practice among the old *Bri-
tifh* nurfes; they have, indeed, been
always the firft preceptors of the youth
of this kingdom, and from them the
rudiments of tafte and learning are
naturally derived. Let none therefore fpeak irreverently of this antient
maternity, as they may be confidered
as the great grandmothers of fcience
and knowledge.

Mother

Mother *GOOSE's Melody.*

A LOVE SONG.

THERE was a little Man,
  Who wooed a little Maid;
And he said, little Maid, will you
  wed, wed, wed?
I have little more to fay,
So will you aye or nay,
For the leaft faid is foonest mended,
  ded, ded.

      II. Then

II.

Then replied the little maid,
Little Sir, you've little said
To induce a little maid for to wed,
    wed, wed;
You muſt ſay a little more,
And produce a little ore,
E're I make a little print in your bed,
    bed, bed.

III.

Then the little man replied,
If you'll be my little bride,
I'll raiſe my love notes a little higher,
    higher, higher;
Tho'. my offers are not meet,
Yet my little heart is great,
With the little god of love all on
    fire, fire, fire.

IV.

Then the little maid replied,
Should I be your little bride,

                    Pray

Pray what muſt we have for to eat,
  eat, eat?
Will the flame that you're ſo rich in
Light a fire in the kitchen,
Or the little god of love turn the
  ſpit, ſpit, ſpit?
    V.
Then the little man he ſigh'd,
And, ſome ſay, a little cry'd,
For his little heart was big with ſor-
  row, ſorrow, ſorrow;
As I'm your little ſlave,
If the little that I have
Be too little, little, we will borrow,
  borrow, borrow*.

 * He who borrows is another man's
ſlave, and pawns his honour, his li-
berty, and ſometimes his noſe for
the payment. Learn to live on a
little and be independent.
    Patch on Prudence.
     VI. Then

VI.

Then the little man ſo gent,
Made the little maid relent.
And ſet her little heart a think kin,
   kin, kin.
Tho' his offers were but ſmall,
She took his little all,
She could have but the cat and her
   ſkin, ſkin, ſkin.

A D I R G E.

LITTLE *Betty Winkle* she had a
pig,
It was a little pig not very big;
When he was alive he liv'd in clover,
But now he's dead and that's all over;
Johnny Winckle he
Sat down and cry'd,
Betty Whickle she
Laid down and dy'd;

So

So there was an end of one, two,
  and three,
Johnny Winckle he,
Betty Winckle she,
And Piggy Wiggie.

 A dirge is a song made for the
dead; but whether this was made for
Betty Winckle or her pig, is uncertain;
no notice being taken of it by *Cam-*
den, or any of the famous Antiqua-
rians.

      Wall's System of Sense.

A Melancholy SONG.

TRIP upon Trenchers,
  And dance upon Diſhes,
My Mother ſent me for ſome **Bawm**,
  ſome Bawm :
She bid me tread lightly,
And come again quickly,
For fear the young Men ſhould do me
  ſome Harm.
Yet didn't you ſee,
Yet didn't you ſee,
What naughty Tricks they put upon
  me ;   B   They

They broke my Pitcher,
And fpilt the Water,
And hufft my Mother,
And chid her Daughter,
And kifs'd my Sifter inftead of me.

What a fucceffion of misfortunes
befell this poor girl? But the laft
circumftance was the moft affecting,
and might have proved fatal.

Winflow's View of Bath.

CROSS

CROSS patch, draw the latch,
 Set by the fire and spin ;
Take a cup and drink it up,
 Then call your neighbours in.

A common case this, to call in our
neighbours to rejoice when all the
good liquor is gone. *Pliny.*

B3   AMPHION's

AMPHION's SONG *of* EURYDICE.

I WON'T be my father's Jack,
 I won't be my father's Gill,
I will be the fidler's wife,
 And have mufic when I will.
  T'other little tune,
  T'other little tune,
  Prithee, Love, play me,
  T'other little tune.

Maxim. Thofe arts are the moft
valuable which are of the greateft ufe.

THREE

THREE wife men of *Gotham,*
    They went to fea in a bowl,
And if the bowl had been ftronger,
My fong had been longer.

It is long enough. Never lament
the lofs of what is not worth having.
Boyle.

B 3   THERE,

THERE was an old man,
  And he had a calf,
  And that's half;
He took him out of the ftall,
And put him on the wall,
  And that's all.

  Maxim. Thofe who are given to
tell all they know, generally tell more
than they know.

THERE

THERE was an old woman
Liv'd under a hill,
She put a moufe in a bag,
And fent it to mill :
The miller did fwear
By the point of his knife,
He never took toll
Of a moufe in his life

The only inftance of a miller re-
fufing toll, and for which the cat
has juft caufe of complaine againft
him.　　　　*Coke* upon *Littleton.*

B4　　　THERE

THERE was an old woman
  Liv'd under a hill,
And if she isn't-gone
She lives there still.

This is a self-evident propofition,
which is the very effence of truth.
She lived under the hill, and if she is not
gone she lives there still. No-body will
presume to contradict this.

Cr.enja'

PLATO's

PLATO's SONG.

DING dong bell,
   The cat is in the well.
Who put her in ?
Little *Johnny Green.*
What a naughty boy was that,
To drown poor Pufly cat.
Who never did any harm,
And kill'd the mice in his father
    barn.

   Maxim. He that injures one
threatens an hundred.

LITTLE

LITTLE *Tom Tucker*
Sings for his supper;
What shall he eat?
White bread and butter:
How will he cut it,
Without e'er a knife?
How will he be married,
Without e'er a wife?

To be married without a wife is a terrible thing, and to be married with a bad wife is something worse; however, a good wife that sings well is the best musical instrument in the world.   *Puffendorf.*

S E faw, *Margery Daw,*
   Jacky fhall have a new mafter;
Jacky muft have but a penny a day,
   Becaufe he can work no faſter.

It is a mean and fcandalous practice in authors to put notes to things
that deferve no notice,

              Grotius

            GREAT

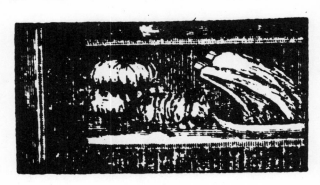

GREAT A, little a,
  Bouncing B ;
The cat's in the cupboard,
And she can't fee.

Yes, she can _ fee that you are
naughty, and don't mind your book.

SE saw, sacaradown,
  Which is the way to *London*
    town?
One foot up, the other foot down,
That is the way to *London* town.

  Or to any other town upon the
face of the earth. *Wickliffe.*

SHOE the colt,
Shoe the colt,
Shoe the wild mare;
Here a nail,
There a nail,
Yet she goes bare.

Ay, ay, drive the nail that will go: that's the way of the world, and is the method pursued by all our financiers, politicians, and necromancers. *Vattel.*

IS

IS *John Smith* within ?
   Yes, that he is.
Can he set a shoe ?
Aye, marry two.
Here a nail and there a nail,
Tick, tack, too.

   Maxim. Knowledge is a treasure, but practice is the key to it.

HIGH

HIGH diddle-diddle,
   The cat and the fiddle,
The cow jump'd over the moon;
The little dog laugh'd
To fee fuch craft,
   And the difh ran away with the
     fpoon.

**It muft be a little dog that laugh'd,
for a great dog would be affamed to
laugh at fuch nonfenfe.**

1   **RIDE**

R IDE a cock horfe
     To *Banbury* crofs,
   To fee what *Tommy* can buy,
A penny white loaf,
A penny white cake,
   And a two-penny apple-pye.

   There's a good boy, eat up your
pye and hold your tongue; for filence
is the fign of wifdom.

COCK

COCK a doodle doo,
  My dame has loſt her ſhoe ;
My maſter has loſt his fiddle ſtick,
And knows not what to do.

The cock crows us up early in
the morning, that we may work for our
bread, and not live upon charity or
upon truſt : *for he who lives upon
charity ſhall be often affronted, and he
that lives upon truſt ſhall pay double.*

4

THERE

THERE was an old man
    In a velvet coat,
He kiss'd a maid
And gave her a groat;
The groat it was crack'd,
And would not go,
Ah, old man, do you serve me so

Maxim.

If the coat be ever so fine that a
fool wears, it is still but a fool's coat

C 2   ROUND

ROUND about, round about,
    Magotty pye;
My Father loves good ale,
    And so do I.

Maxim.

Evil company makes the good
bad, and the bad worse.

JACK

J*ACK* and *Gill*
　　Went up the hill,
　To fetch a pail of water;
Jack fell down
And broke his crown,
　And *Gill* came tumbling after.

Maxim.

The more you think of dying, the
letter you will live.

C 3　　　　　　Ans-

ARISTOTLE's STORY.

THERE were two birds sat on a
    Stone.
  Fa, la, la, la, lal, de;
One flew away, and then there was one,
  Fa, la, la, la, lal, de;
The other flew after,
And then there was none,
  Fa, la, la, la, lal, de;
And so the poor stone
Was left all alone,
  Fa, la, la, la, lal, de;

  This may serve as a chapter of
consequence in the next new book of
logic.   *Sewall's* Reports

HUSH-a-by baby
   On the tree top,
When the wind blows
   The cradle will rock;
When the bough breaks
   The cradle will fall,
Down tumbles baby,
   Cradle and all.
   This may ferve as a warning to
the proud and ambitious, who climb
fo high that they generally fall at laft.

Maxim.

   Content turns all it touches into
gold.

C 4   **LITTLE**

LITTLE *Jack Horner*
 Sat in a corner,
 Eating of *Christmas* pye;
He put in his thumb,
And pull'd out a plumb,
 And what a good boy was I.

 Jack was a boy of excellent taste, as should appear by his pulling out a plumb; it is therefore supposed that his father apprenticed him to a mince pye-maker, that he might improve his taste from year to year; no one standing in so much need of good taste as a pastry cook.

Bexley on the Sublime and Beautiful.
 PEASE

PEASE-porridge hot
     Peaſe-porridge cold,
Peaſe-porridge in the pot
     Nine days old,
Spell me that in four letters ;
     I will, THAT.

Maxim.

The poor are ſeldomer ſick for
want of food, than the rich are by
the exceſs of it.

WHO

W HO comes here?
　　A grenadier.
What do you want?
　A pot of beer.
Where is your money?
　I've forgot.
Get you gone
　You drunken ~~sot~~. *sot,*

Maxim.

Intemperance is attended with difcafes, and idlenefs with poverty.

JACK

J ACK *Sprat*
   Could eat no fat,
  His wife could eat no lean;
And so betwixt them both,
   They lick'd the platter clean.

Maxim.

Better to go to bed supperless, ▬▬
rise in debt:

WHAT

WHAT care I how black I be,
    Twenty pounds will marry
  me ;
If twenty won't, forty fhall,
I am my mother's bouncing girl.

Maxim.

If we do not flatter ourfelves, the
flattery of others would have no effect.

TELL

TELL tale tit,
    Your tongue ſhall be ſlit,
And all the dogs in our town
   Shall have a bit.

Maxim.

Point not at the faults of others
with a foul finger.

ONE

ONE, two, three,
    Four and five,
I caught a hare alive;
Six, seven, eight,
Nine and ten,
I let him go again.

Maxim.

We may be as good as we please,
If we please to be good.

THREE

A DOLEFUL DITTY.

I.

THREE children sliding on the ice
    Upon a summer's day,
As it fell out they all fell in,
    The rest they ran away.

II.

Oh! had these children been at
    school,
    Or sliding on dry ground,
Ten thousand pounds to one penny,
    They had not then been drown'd.

              III. Ye

III.

Ye parents who have children dear,
 And eke ye that have none,
If you would keep them safe abroad,
 Pray keep them safe at home.

There is something so melancholy
in this song, that it has occasioned
many people to make water. It is
almost as diuretic as the tune which
John the coachman whistles to his
horses. *Trumpington*'s Travels.

PATTY

PATTY cake, patty cake,
  Bakers man;
That I will master,
As fast as I can;
Prick it, and prick it,
And mark it with a T,
And there will be enough
For *Jacky* and me.

Maxim.

The surest way to gain our ends is
to moderate our desires.
                    D   WHEN

WHEN I was a little boy
    I had but little wit,
'Tis a long time ago,
    And I have no more yet;
Nor ever, ever shall,
    Until that I die,
For the longer I live,
    The more fool am I.

Maxim.

He that will be his own master,
has often a fool for his scholar.
              WHEN

I.

WHEN I was a little boy
    I liv'd by myfelf,
And all the bread
And cheefe I got
    I laid upon the fhelf;
The rats and the mice
    They made fuch a ftrife,
That I was forc'd to go to town
    And buy me a wife.

II.

The ftreets were fo broad,
    The lanes were fo narrow,

D 2   I was

I was forc'd to bring my wife home
   In a wheel-barrow ;
The wheel-barrow broke,
   And my wife had a fall,
——————Farewell
Wheel-barrow wife and all.

Maxim.

Provide against the worst, and hope
for the best.

O my

O My kitten a kitten,
 And oh! my kitten, my deary,
Such a sweet pap as this
There is not far nor neary;
There we go up, up, up,
Here we go down, down, down,
Here we go backwards and forwards,
And here we go round, round, round.

Maxim.

Idleneſs hath no advocate, but
many friends.

D 3   **THIS**

THIS pig went to market,
   'That pig ſtaid at home ;
This pig had roaſt meat,
That pig had none ;
This pig went to the barn-door,
And cry'd week, 'week, for more.

Maxim.

If we do not govern our paſſions
our paſſions will govern us.

THERE

ALEXANDER's SONG.

THERE was a man of *Theſſaly*,
 And he was wondrous wiſe,
He jump'd into a quick-ſet hedge,
 And ſcratch'd out both his eyes:
And when he ſaw his eyes were out,
 With all his might and main,
He jump'd into another hedge,
 And ſcratch'd them in again.

D 4   How

How happy it was for the man to
ſcratch his eyes in again, when they
were ſcratch'd out! But he was a
blockhead or he would have kept
himſelf out of the hedge, and not
been ſcratch'd at all.

Wiſeman's new Way to Wiſdom.

A Long

A Long tail'd pig, or a short
tail'd pig,
Or a pig without any tail;
A sow pig, or a boar pig,
Or a pig with a curling tail.

Take hold of the tail and eat off his
head;
And then you'll be sure the pig-hog
is dead.

CÆSAR'

CÆSAR's SONG.

BOW, wow, wow,
  Whose dog art thou?
Little *Tom Tinker's* dog,
Bow, wow, wow.

Tom Tinker's dog is a very good
dog, and an honester dog than his
master.

BAH,

BAH, bah, black fheep,
  Have you any wool?
Yes, marry have I,
  Three bags full;
One for my mafter,
  One for my dame,
But none for the little boy
  Who cries in the lane.

Maxim.

Bad habits are eafier conquered to
day than to-morrow.

ROBIN

ROBIN and *Richard*
    Were two preity men,
They lay in bed
    'Till the clock ftruck ten :
Then up ftarts *Robin*
    And looks at the fky,
Oh! brother *Richard,*
    The fun's very high ;
You go before
    With the bottle and bag,
And I will come after
    On little *Jack* nag

What

What lazy rogues were thefe to lie in bed fo long, I dare fay they have no cloaths to their backs; for *lazinefs cloaths a man with rags.*

THERE

THERE was an old woman,
    And she sold puddings and pies,
She went to the mill
    And the dust flew into her eyes:
Hot pies,
    And cold pies to sell,
Wherever she goes
    You may follow her by the smell.

Maxim.

Either say nothing of the absent,
or speak like a friend.

THERE

THERE were two blackbirds
    Sat upon a hill,
The one was nam'd *Jack*,
    The other nam'd *Gill*;
Fly away *Jack*,
    Fly away *Gill*,
Come again *Jack*,
    Come again *Gill*.

Maxim.

A bird in the hand is worth two in
the bush

THE

THE sow came in with a saddle,
   The little pig rock'd the cradle,
The dish jump'd a top of the table,
To fee the pot wash the ladle;
The spit that stood behind the door
Call'd the dishclout dirty whore:
Ods-plut, says the gridiron,
   Can't ye agree,
I'm the head conftable,
   Bring 'em to me.

   * *Note,* If he acts as conftable in this cafe, the cook muft furely be the juftice of peace.

BOYS

BOYS and girls come out to play,
The moon does fhine as bright
  as day;
Come with a hoop, and come with a
  call,
Come with a good will or not at all.
Loofe your fupper, and loofe your
  fleep,
Come to your playfellows in the
  ftreet;
Up the ladder and down the wall
A halfpenny loaf will ferve us all.

     E   But

But when the loaf is gone, what will
you do?
Thofe who would eat muft work.

Maxim.

All work and no play makes *Jack*
a dull boy.

WERE

WE'RE three brethren out of
Spain
Come to court your daughter *Jane:*
My daughter *Jane* she is too young,
She has no skill in a flattering tongue.
Be she young, or be she old,
Its for her gold she must be sold;
So fare you well my lady gay,
We must return another day.

                    Maxim.

Riches serve a wise man, and govern a fool.

                E 2   *A Logical*

A Logical SONG; *or the* CONJU-ROR'S *Reason for not getting Money.*

I Would, it I cou'd,
   If I cou'dn't, how cou'd I ?
I cou'dn't, without I cou'd, cou'd I ?
Cou'd you, without you cou'd, cou'd
      ye ?
   Cou'd ye, Cou'd ye ?
Cou'd you, without you cou'd, cou'd
      ye ?

Note

Note.

This is a new way of handling an old argument, said to be invented by a famous senator; but it has something in it of *Gothic* construction.

Sanderson.

A LEARN-

A LEARNED SONG.

HERE's A, B, and C,
 D, E, F, and G,
H, I, K, L, M, N, O, P, Q,
 R, S, T, and U,
W, X, Y, and Z.
And here's the child's dad,
Who is fagacious and difcerning,
And knows this is the fount of learn-
 ing.

Note

Note.

This is the moſt learned ditty in the world: for indeed there is no ſong can be made without the aid of this, it being the *gamut* and ground-work of them all.

Mope's Geography of the **Mind.**

E 4   *A* SEASON-

A SEASONABLE SONG.

PIPING hot, smoaking hot,
    What I've got,
You have not,
Hot grey peale, hot, hot, hot;
Hot grey pease hot.

    There is more music in this song,
an a cold frosty night, than ever the
Syrens were possessed of, who capti-
vated *Ulyss;* and the effects stick
closer to the ribs.
               Hugglesford on Hunger.
               DICKERY,

DICKERY, dickery, dock,
    The moufe ran up the clock;
The clock ftruck one,
The moufe ran down,
Dickery, dickery dock.

Maxim.

Time fays for no man,

✖✖✖✖✖✖✖✖✖✖✖✖✖

MOTHER GOOSE's
MELODY,
PART II.
CONTAINING THE
LULLABIES of *Shakespeare.*

✖✖✖✖✖✖✖✖✖✖✖✖✖

✖✖✖✖✖✖✖8✖✖✖✖✖✖✖

WHERE the bee fucks, there
fuck I,
In a cowflip's bell I lie:
There I couch, when owls do cry,
On the bat's back I do fly,
After fummer, merrily.
Merrily, merrily fhall I live now,
Under the bloffom that hangs on the
bough.

YOU

YOU fpotted fnakes, with dou-
     ble tongue ;
  Thorny hedge hogs be not feen ;
Newts and blind-worms, do no
     wrong ; *
  Come not near our fairy queen.
Philomel, with melody,
Sing in your fweet lullaby ;
Lulla, lulla, lulla, lullaby ; lulla,
     lulla, lullaby.
Never harm, nor fpell, nor charm,
Come our lovely lady nigh ;
So good night, with lullaby.

TAKE,

TAKE, oh! take thofe lips away,
  That fo fweetly were for-fworn;
And thofe eyes, the break of day,
  Lights that do miflead the morn:
But my kiffes bring again,
Seals of love, but feal'd in vain.

SPRING

SPRING.

WHEN daifes pied, and violets
  blue,
And lady-fmocks all filver-white;
And cuckow-buds of yellow hue,
Do paint the meadows with delight:
The cuckow then on every tree,
Mocks married men, for thus fings he;
Cuckow!
Cuckow! cuckow! O word of fear,
Unpleafing to a married ear!
When fhepherds pipe on oaten ftraws,
  And merry larks are plough-men's
    clocks:
When turtles tread, and rooks and
    daws,
  And maiden's bleach their fummer
    fmocks;
The cuckow then on every tree,
Mocks married men, for thus fings he;
Cuckow!
Cuckow! cuckow! O word of fear,
Unpleafing to a married ear.

WINTER.

WHEN icicles hang on the wall,
    And *Dick* the fhepherd blows
      his nail ;
And *Tom* bears logs into the hall,
    And milk comes frozen home in
      pail :
When blood is nipt, and ways be foul,
Then nightly fings the ftaring owl,
Tu-whit ! to-whoo ;
    A merry note,
    While greafy *Joan* doth keel the
      pot.
When all around the wind doth blow,
    And coughing drowns the parfon's
      faw ;
And birds fit brooding in the fnow,
    And *Marian's* nofe looks red and
      raw :

When

When roasted crabs hiss in the bowl,
Then nightly sings the staring owl,
Tu-whit! To-whoo!
  A merry note,
  While greasy *Joan* doth keel the
    pot.

TELL me where is fancy bred,
　　Or in the heart or in the head?
How begot, how nourished?
Reply, reply.
It is engendered in the eyes,
With gazing fed, and fancy die
In the cradle where it lies;
Let us all ring fancy's knell,
Ding, dong, bell;
Ding, dong, bell.

UNDER

UNDER the greenwood tree,
  Who loves to lie with me,
And tune his merry note,
Unto the sweet bird's throat:
Come hither, come hither, come
      hither.
  Here shall he see
  No enemy,
But winter and rough weather.

WHO

WHO doth ambition fhun,
    And loves to lie i' th' fun,
Seeking the food he eats,
And pleas'd with what he gets;
Come hither, come hither, come
        hither;
    Here fhall he fee
    No enemy,
But winter and rough weather.

If it do come to pafs
That any man turn afs;
Leaving his wealth and eafe,
A ftubborn will to pleafe,
Duc ad me, duc ad me, duc ad me;
    Here fhall he fee
    Grofs fools,
And if he will come to me.

BLOW

BLOW, blow, thou winter wind,
   Thou art not ſo unkind
  As man's ingratitude:
Thy tooth is not ſo keen,
Becauſe thou art not ſeen,
  Although thy breath be rude.
Heigh ho! ſing, heigh ho! unto the
     green holly!
Moſt friendſhip is feigning; moſt lov-
   ing mere folly.
   Then heigh ho, the holly!
   This life is moſt jolly.

Freeze, freeze, thou bitter ſky,
That doſt not bite ſo nigh,
  As benefits forgot:
Tho' thou the waters warp,
Thy ſting is not ſo ſharp
  As friend remember'd not.
Heigh-ho! ſing, &c.

                    O Mil-

O Miftrefs mine, where are you
    running ?
O ftay and hear your true love's
  coming,
   That can fing both high and low.
Trip no further, pretty fweeting,
Journey's end in lover's meeting,
   Every wife man's fon doth know.
What is love ? 'tis not hereafter;
Prefent mirth has prefent laughter.
   What's to come, is ftill unfure;
In decay there lies no plenty;
Then come kifs me, fweet and twenty,
   Youth's a ftuff will not endure.

WHAT

WHAT shall he have that kill'd
      the deer?
His leather skin and horns to wear;
Then sing him home:—take thou no
    scorn
To wear the horn, the horn, the⎫
   horn: ⎪
It was a crest ere thou wast born. ⎬
Thy father's father wore it,   ⎪
And thy father bore it.   ⎭
The horn, the horn, the lusty horn,
Is not a thing to laugh to scorn.

WHEN

WHEN daffodils begin to 'pear,
    With, heigh! the doxy over
    the dale;
Why then come in the sweet o'th'
    year,
    'Fore the red blood rains-in the
    winter pale,
The white sheet bleaching on the
    hedge,
    With heigh the sweet birds, O how
    they sing!
Doth set my progging tooth an edge:
    For a quart of ale is a dish for a
    king.
The lark that tirra-lyra chants,
    With, hey! with hey! the thrush
    and the jay:
    Are summer songs for me and my
    aunts,
    While we lay tumbling in the hay.

JOG

JOG on, jog on, the foot path way,
   And merrily hent the ſtyle-a,
A merry heart goes all the day,
   Your ſad tires in a mile-a.

ORPHEUS

ORPHEUS with his lute made trees,
And the mountain tops that freeze,
  Bow themfelves when he did fing;
To his mufic, plants and flowers
Ever rofe, as fun and fhowers
  There had made a lafting fpring.

Ev'ry thing that heard him play,
Ev'n the billows of the fea,
  Hung their heads, and then lay by.
In fweet mufic is fuch art,
Killing care, and grief of heart,
  Fall afleep or hearing die.

HARK

HARK, hark! the lark at hea-
    ven's gate sings,
  And *Phœbus* 'gins arise,
His steeds to water at those springs
  On chalic'd flowers that lies,
And winking may-buds begin
  To ope their golden eyes,
With every thing that pretty bin
  My lady sweet arise:
    Arise, arise.

THE

THE poor foul fat finging by a
     fycamore-tree,
Her hand on her bofom, her head on
     her knee,
The fresh streams ran by her, and
     murmur'd her moans,
Her foft tears fell from her, and
     foften'd the ftones;
  Sing all a green willow muft be my
     garland,
Let nobody blame him, his fcorn I
     approve.
I call'd my love falfe love, but what
     faid he then?
If I court more women you'll think
     of more men.

F I N I S.